VOCABULARY SPELLING Poetry II

Fifth Edition

abeka
Pensacola, FL 32523-9100
an affiliate of PENSACOLA CHRISTIAN COLLEGE®

Pronunciation Key

Symbol	Example	Symbol	Example
ā	āte	ŏ	nŏt
â	dâre	oi	boil
ă	făt	o͞o	fo͞od
ä	fäther	o͝o	bo͝ok
ə	ago (ə·gō′)	ou	out
ē	ēven	th	thin
ĕ	ĕgg	t̶h̶	t̶h̶ere
ẽ (ər)	pondẽr	tū	pictūre
ī	īce	ū	ūnit
ĭ	ĭt	û	hûrt
ō	ōver	ŭ	ŭp
ô	côrd, taught, saw	zh	measure

Vocabulary, Spelling, Poetry II
Fifth Edition

Staff Credits
Author: James A. Chapman
Edition Editor: Sandra Brazil
Cover Designers: Shawn Thayer, Michelle Johnson
Designer: Michelle Johnson

Abeka, a Christian textbook ministry affiliated with Pensacola Christian College, is designed to meet the need for Christian textbooks and teaching aids. The purpose of this publishing ministry is to help Christian schools reach children and young people for the Lord and train them in the Christian way of life.

Photo credit: cover and title page—©istockphoto.com / Susan Trigg

"Stopping by Woods on a Snowy Evening" from *The Poetry of Robert Frost* edited by Edward Connery Lathem. Copyright 1923, 1969 by Henry Holt and Company. Copyright 1951 by Robert Frost. Reprinted by permission of Henry Holt and Company, LLC.

Cataloging Data

Chapman, James A. (James Aaron), 1940-
Vocabulary, spelling, poetry II / James A. Chapman.—5th ed.
82 p. : col. ill. ; 23 cm.
1. English language—Orthography and spelling (Secondary),
2. Vocabulary—Study and teaching (Secondary) III. Abeka Book, Inc.
Library of Congress PE 1145.2 .C53 2009
Dewey System 428.82

Contents

Poetry

First Nine Weeks

Second Nine Weeks

Third Nine Weeks

Fourth Nine Weeks

Four Spelling Rules to Master

1 *i* before *e* except after *c* or when sounded like *ā* as in neighbor and weigh.

i before ***e:*** achi**ie**ve, bri**ie**f, fi**ie**rce, shri**ie**k, thi**ie**f
except after ***c:*** c**ei**ling, conc**ei**t, dec**ei**ve, perc**ei**ve, rec**ei**ve
sounded like ***ā:*** f**ei**gn, fr**ei**ght, h**ei**nous, r**ei**gn, v**ei**l

Some common exceptions are illustrated in this sentence: N**ei**ther financ**ie**r s**ei**zed **ei**ther w**ei**rd spec**ie**s of l**ei**sure.

Other exceptions can be easily memorized. In the spelling lists in this book, an asterisk (*) indicates each exception to the rule.

2 Double the final consonant before a suffix beginning with a vowel if the word has only one syllable or is accented on the last syllable and thc word ends in a single consonant preceded by a single vowel.

One-syllable words: plan, pla**nn**ed; ship, shi**pp**ed; brag, bra**gg**ing; rob, ro**bb**er; hop, ho**pp**ed

Last syllable accented: be**gin,** begi**nn**ing; re**fer,** refe**rr**ing; com**mit,** commi**tt**ed; for**bid,** forbi**dd**en; con**fer,** confe**rr**ed

Last syllable not accented: **mar**vel, marve**l**ed; **coun**sel, counse**l**ed; **tra**vel, trave**l**ed

Not ending in single consonant preceded by single vowel: cra**mp,** cram**p**ed; l**oo**k, loo**k**ed

3 For words ending in *y* preceded by a consonant, change the *y* to *i* before all suffixes except those beginning with *i*.

Suffixes not beginning with *i:* try, tried; busy, busily; accompany, accompanied

Suffixes beginning with *i:* try, trying; busy, busying; accompany, accompanying

Final *y* preceded by vowel: turkey, turkeys; attorney, attorneys; employ, employs

4 In adding a suffix to a word ending in silent *e*, retain the *e* if the suffix begins with a consonant, but drop the *e* if the suffix begins with a vowel.

Suffix beginning with consonant: arrang**e***m*ent, complet**e***ly*, lik**e***ly*

Suffix beginning with vowel: arrang*ing*, complet*ing*, lik*ing*

Common exceptions:

(1) Drop the final ***e*** when *-ment* is added to words ending in ***dge:*** ju**dge**, ju**dg***ment;* acknowle**dge**, acknowl-e**dg***ment*

(2) Retain the final ***e*** in words ending in ***ce*** or ***ge*** when *-able* or *-ous* is added: trac**e***able,* charg**e***able,* coura-g**e***ous,* outrag**e***ous.*

Other exceptions can be easily memorized. In the spelling lists in this book, an asterisk (*) indicates each exception to the rule.

Keys to Good Spelling

1 Realize that when two words are compounded (put together as one), the spelling of the two parts does not change.

ear + ring = ea**rr**ing   lamp + post = lam**pp**ost

2 Realize that when a prefix is added to a word, the spelling of the word itself does not change.

il + legal = il**legal**   dis + satisfied = dis**satisfied**

3 Learn and apply the spelling rules on pages 4 and 5.

4 Spell by syllables and say the word aloud or in your mind as the word will be written, not as it may be pronounced. For example, the word *Wednesday* is pronounced something like "Wenzdi"; but if you pronounce the word as it will be written, you will pronounce it "Wed-nes-day." Put this principle into practice like this:

a. While looking steadfastly at the word, say the word aloud or in your head syllable by syllable. For example, for the word *consolidated,* say "con-sol-i-da-ted."

b. Look away from the word and write "con-sol-i-da-ted," saying and then writing one syllable at a time, of course connecting the syllables as you write them.

c. Look back at the word that you have written and compare it syllable by syllable to the word in your book.

d. If you made a mistake in the spelling, repeat the process described in *a* through *c* above until you can spell the word correctly.

Certain words are difficult to say as written. For these words, you must be careful to **see** the letters in the word that are difficult to **say,** for example, the *k* in *knit* and the *tion* in *intention.* If you can see the *k* in *knit,* you can just say **nit,** instead of **k**-nit. If you can see the *tion* in *intention,* you can just say **tion** ("shun") instead of **ti-on.** Also, some words have a sound that can be pronounced more than one way, for example the first *c* in *catch.* In order to spell the word correctly with a *c* and not a *k,* you must be careful to **see** the *c;* and then your brain will remember the correct letter.

5 Learn to distinguish between homophones. (A **homophone** is one of two or more words that have the same sound but differ in spelling, origin, and meaning.) In order to spell these words correctly, you simply have to memorize their variant spellings and meanings. Here are some examples of homophones:

aid / aide	council / counsel	threw / through
ball / bawl	die / dye	waist / waste
bough / bow	heal / heel	whose / who's

6 Learn lists of commonly misspelled words. (See the lists of such words in this book.)

7 Keep a list of your own spelling errors, and go over the correct spellings from time to time.

LIST 1

Spelling

Compound words and words with prefixes (See "Keys to Good Spelling" numbers 1 and 2 on page 6.)

1. **bookkeeper**
2. **cattail**
3. **disservice**
4. **dissimilar**
5. **earrings**
6. **fishhook**
7. **foolhardy**
8. **illegible**
9. **immortal**
10. **innumerable**
11. **irrelevant**
12. **nighttime**
13. **overrun**
14. **roommate**
15. **unnamed**
16. **unnecessary**
17. **unnerve**
18. **videotape**
19. **whichever**
20. **yardstick**

Vocabulary

1. **chamois** (shăm′ē), n. **soft leather used for cleaning**

   A ***chamois*** is usually made from the skins of the chamois, a goat-like animal.

2. **guile** (gīl), n. **skillful or cunning use of deceit**

   The conman practiced his ***guile*** on the unsuspecting tourists.

3. **integrity** (ĭn·tĕg′rĭ·tē), n. **moral soundness, honesty**

   How we need men of ***integrity*** in our Congress these days!

4. **irrepressible** (ĭr′rē·prĕs′ə·bəl), adj. **unrestrainable, uncontrollable**

   Mrs. McCray felt an ***irrepressible*** urge to care for the orphans.

5. **meticulous** (mĭ·tĭk′yə·ləs), adj. **careful, accurate**

   Through the ***meticulous*** restoration of famous homesteads, Henry Ford preserved a part of our American heritage.

6. **obscurity** (ŏb·skyo͝or′ĭ·tē), n. **the condition of being unknown**

   Emily Dickinson, a great American poet, died in ***obscurity.***

7. **perspective** (pĕr·spĕk′tĭv), n. **point of view**

   From my ***perspective,*** I believe that he made the right decision.

8. **scrutinize** (skro͞o′tĭ·nīz), v. **closely examine**

   A good machinist will ***scrutinize*** his work to catch imperfections.

9. **steadfast** (stĕd′făst), adj. **firmly established, unwavering**

   According to Hebrews 6:19, the hope which God gives provides a sure and ***steadfast*** anchor for the soul.

10. **tolerate** (tŏl′ər·āt), v. **allow, permit**

    One should learn to ***tolerate*** differences of opinion.

Exercises

A

In the blank provided, write the word from vocabulary list 1 that best completes each sentence. (Note: You may have to change the tense or form of the word.)

1. The native Texan could not tolerate Michigan's cold weather.
2. Nineveh was lost in obscurity until its ruins were discovered hundreds of years later.
3. Anyone who has a(n) steadfast thirst for knowledge will not be denied.
4. Better is the poor that walketh in his integrity, than he that is perverse in his lips, and is a fool. *—Prov. 19:1*
5. A chamois is great for drying cars because of its absorbency.
6. Marco Polo's meticulous record of his journeys enabled men to develop maps of East Asia.
7. The authorities scrutinize the evidence to solve the case.
8. The Bible instructs Christians to be steadfast and unmovable in their faith.

B

In each of the following groups, circle the word that is most nearly a ***synonym*** *of the italicized vocabulary word in the introductory phrase.*

1. a *meticulous* housekeeper
   (a) precise (b) valuable (c) congenial (d) dependable
2. remaining *steadfast* concerning principles
   (a) diplomatic (b) enthusiastic (c) serious (d) constant
3. unquestioned *integrity*
   (a) earnestness (b) uprightness (c) calmness (d) pleasantness
4. to *scrutinize* the manuscript
   (a) inspect (b) notice (c) condense (d) display
5. should never *tolerate* treason
   (a) provoke (b) accept (c) initiate (d) inhibit
6. full of *guile*
   (a) honesty (b) bitterness (c) discernment (d) deception
7. the proper *perspective*
   (a) standpoint (b) proposal (c) decision (d) pattern

Spelling

Words illustrating rule 1
(See page 4.)

1 **achievement**
2 **believe**
3 **besiege**
4 **ceiling**
5 **chief**
6 **conceive**
7 **deceit**
8 **eighth**
9 **financier***
10 **leisure***
11 **lieutenant**
12 **neighing**
13 **niece**
14 **receipt**
15 **reign**
16 **relieve**
17 **transceiver**
18 **vein**
19 **view**
20 **weird***

Note: An asterisk (*) indicates an exception to the rule.

Vocabulary

1. **accelerate** (ăk·sĕl′ə·rāt′), v. **move or develop faster**
   The car will ***accelerate*** when traveling downhill.

2. **alleged** (ə·lĕjd′), adj. **assumed or supposed, accused without proof**
   The ***alleged*** murderer's trial begins in two months.

3. **demeanor** (dĭ·mēn′ẽr), n. **outward bearing or behavior**
   Paul hoped that Timothy would have such a good ***demeanor*** that no one would think poorly of him because of his youth.

4. **inflexible** (ĭn·flĕk′sə·bəl), adj. **firm in will or purpose, unyielding**
   It is good to be ***inflexible*** concerning the authority of God's Word.

5. **irreverent** (ĭ·rĕv′ər·ənt), adj. **disrespectful, lacking appropriate seriousness**
   The ***irreverent*** boy refused to salute the flag.

6. **ludicrous** (lo͞o′dĭ·krəs), adj. **laughable, ridiculous**
   It is ***ludicrous*** for any Christian to fight Satan in his own strength.

7. **sullen** (sŭl′ən), adj. **ill-humoredly unsociable, gloomily silent**
   Because the child could not do what he wanted, he became ***sullen.***

8. **sumptuous** (sŭmp′cho͞o·əs), adj. **costly, splendid, luxurious**
   Unlike the beggar Lazarus, the rich man had ***sumptuous*** meals every day.

9. **tangible** (tăn′jə·bəl), adj. **touchable**
   If an infant is not given ***tangible*** objects to play with, he will play with sunbeams or shadows.

10. **valor** (văl′ər), n. **bravery, gallantry, heroism**
    True ***valor*** is facing danger even when afraid.

Exercises

List 2

A *From vocabulary list 2, choose the word that best completes each sentence. (Note: You may have to change the tense or form of the word.)*

1. The ____________________ life of a king or queen is difficult for the ordinary person to imagine.
2. Newscasters have to be careful to say that a suspect is a(n) ____________________ criminal until he is convicted of the crime.
3. Playing around in church reveals a(n) ____________________ attitude.
4. Many people long for something visible and ____________________ as an object of worship.
5. The doctor's grave ____________________ showed that he had been unable to save the dying man.
6. A hero is a person who shows an unusual degree of ____________________ even in the most terrifying of circumstances.
7. The senator remained ____________________ in his stand, responding neither to threats nor promises.
8. We need to ____________________ the processing of these forms.
9. The king was stirred from his ____________________ mood by the court jester.
10. That man could go to the moon was once considered ____________________.

B *Write the vocabulary word from list 2 that is most nearly* ***opposite*** *in meaning to the word at the left.*

1. untouchable ____________________
2. serious ____________________
3. cowardice ____________________
4. honoring ____________________
5. sparing ____________________
6. confirmed ____________________
7. submissive ____________________
8. cheerful ____________________
9. gradual ____________________

Spelling

Words illustrating rule 2 (See page 4.)

1 **abhorrent**
2 **allotted**
3 **annulled**
4 **beginning**
5 **benefited**
6 **compelling**
7 **conferring**
8 **counselor**
9 **equipped**
10 **getting**
11 **grabbed**
12 **marvelous**
13 **occurrence**
14 **patrolled**
15 **perilous**
16 **preferred**
17 **quarreled**
18 **reference**
19 **repelled**
20 **transmitted**

Vocabulary

1. **admonish** (ăd·mŏn′ĭsh), v. **warn, counsel**
   Count him not as an enemy, but ***admonish*** him as a brother. *—2 Thess. 3:15*

2. **aggravate** (ăg′rə·vāt), v. **worsen, intensify**
   Lying to cover a wrong will only ***aggravate*** your guilt.

3. **arbitrary** (är′bĭ·trĕr′ē), adj. **based on whim or chance**
   The dictator's ***arbitrary*** laws harmed many.

4. **chortle** (chôr′tl), n. **joyful chuckle**
   Chortle combines the two words *chuckle* and *snort.*

5. **gallantly** (găl′ənt·lē), adv. **bravely, daringly, dashingly**
   The knight ***gallantly*** fought his enemy in battle.

6. **informality** (ĭn′fôr·măl′ĭ·tē), n. **relaxedness, casualness**
   The man felt out of place in his coat and tie when he noticed the ***informality*** of the occasion.

7. **institute** (ĭn′stĭ·to͞ot), v. **establish, initiate**
   They decided to ***institute*** an inquiry into the organization's finances.

8. **lavish** (lăv′ĭsh), adj. **prodigal, extravagant**
   The ***lavish*** use of our oil supplies has necessitated the need for alternative fuels.

9. **morale** (mə·răl′), n. **spirit, confidence, discipline**
   It is a great advantage to troops in wartime if they can maintain their ***morale.***

10. **stimulus** (stĭm′yə·ləs), n. **goad, spur, incentive**
    An increase of the money supply is usually a ***stimulus*** to business.

Exercises

A *From vocabulary list 3, choose the word that best completes each sentence. (Note: You may have to change the tense or form of the word.)*

1. Sometimes when a rule seems ______________________, we just have to trust God and submit to His authority by obeying it.
2. It became apparent that the company must ______________________ a new method of cost accounting.
3. Please ______________________ your friend not to tell such tall tales about his hunting trips.
4. Todd ______________________ stepped aside to let his best friend have the chance to be class president.
5. Scratching a mosquito bite usually just ______________________ the itching.
6. The friendly ______________________ of the hostess immediately put her guests at ease.
7. The audience erupted with ______________________ when the child tripped in the class play.
8. A good coach realizes that in order to have a winning season he must somehow maintain the ______________________ of his team.
9. There is no ______________________ to improvement like fair competition.
   —Martineau
10. The queen of Sheba presented ______________________ gifts to King Solomon.

B *Circle the vocabulary word in parentheses that best completes the meaning.*

1. Ignoring the problem now will (admonish, aggravate) the difficulty of the solution.
2. It is important that a nation keep up its (stimulus, morale) so that if war becomes necessary the nation can fight to win.
3. The (informality, stimulus) of John's outfit was inappropriate for the banquet.
4. The apostle Paul tells us to (admonish, institute) a brother who does not obey the Word of God.
5. The (arbitrary, informality) decision to buy a new car turned out to be a good decision.

Spelling

Words illustrating rule 3 (See page 5.)

1 **assemblies**
2 **business**
3 **difficulties**
4 **friendliness**[1,3]
5 **glorious**
6 **happiness**
7 **heavily**
8 **hungrily**
9 **liveliness**
10 **loneliness**
11 **merriment**
12 **modifier**
13 **petrified**
14 **qualified**
15 **readily**
16 **satisfied**
17 **theories**
18 **tries**
19 **vacancies**
20 **varies**

Note: A superscript number ([1], [2] etc.) after a word indicates the spelling rule on pages 4–5 which applies.

Vocabulary

1. **accumulate** (ə·kyo͞om′yə·lāt′), v. **collect, gather, increase**
   It is not wise to ***accumulate*** large amounts of debt.

2. **gingerly** (jĭn′jẽr·lē), adv. **carefully, cautiously**
   Trevor ***gingerly*** explored the darkened room, feeling his way around the furniture until he found a flashlight.

3. **irritant** (ĭr′ĭ·tənt), n. **cause of annoyance**
   The pebble in my shoe was an ***irritant.***

4. **lacerate** (lăs′ər·āt), v. **rend, tear, mangle**
   During ground battles, exploding shells ***lacerate*** the countryside.

5. **lament** (lə·mĕnt′), v. **bemoan, bewail**
   Is there not a cause to ***lament*** the lack of personal responsibility in our world today?

6. **loath** (lōth), adj. **reluctant, hesitant, disinclined**
   Grandfather was ***loath*** to part with the old dog.

7. **meditate** (mĕd′ĭ·tāt), v. **muse, think, ponder**
   His delight is in the law of the Lord; and in His law doth he ***meditate*** day and night.
   —*Psa. 1:2*

8. **pretentious** (prĭ·tĕn′shəs), adj. **claiming to be worthy of distinction, showy**
   The ***pretentious*** teen snubbed most of her classmates.

9. **vindictive** (vĭn·dĭk′tĭv), adj. **spiteful, revengeful**
   The ***vindictive*** child hit anyone who tattled on him.

10. **yoke** (yōk), v. **join, attach, connect**
    The Taylors' children love to ***yoke*** their Saint Bernard to a cart and go for a ride.

Exercises

A *From vocabulary list 4, choose the word that best completes each sentence. (Note: You may have to change the tense or form of the word.)*

List 4

1. Granville remained cheerful and did not ____________________ his own misfortune.
2. The Bible warns Christians not to be "unequally ____________________ together with unbelievers."
3. After____________________ testing the water with his paw, the cat stalked away from the fish pond.
4. Because he knew so little English, the immigrant was ____________________ to speak to anyone but his friends.
5. Loud noise from the soccer field sometimes is a(n) ____________________ to the surrounding neighbors.
6. The man's body was ____________________ when he was thrown through the windshield of his car.
7. Mr. Beasley has ____________________ an impressive collection of WWII memorabilia.
8. The ____________________ antiques dealer ignored the shabbily dressed customer.
9. A child of God should never be ____________________ but should have a forgiving spirit.
10. I will ____________________ in Thy precepts, and have respect unto Thy ways. *—Psa. 119:15*

B *Write the vocabulary word from list 4 that is most nearly* ***opposite*** *in meaning to the word or expression at the left.*

1. eager	____________________	5. mend	____________________
2. ignore	____________________	6. carelessly	____________________
3. separate	____________________	7. rejoice	____________________
4. delight	____________________	8. merciful	____________________

Spelling

Words illustrating rule 4 (See page 5.)

1 **absolutely**
2 **admiration**
3 **advertisement**
4 **arguing**
5 **careless**
6 **coarseness**
7 **encouraging**
8 **exploring**
9 **fascinating**
10 **graduating**
11 **immediately**
12 **judgment***
13 **placing**
14 **requirement**
15 **scarcely**
16 **truly***
17 **unfortunately**
18 **using**
19 **wholly**
20 **zoning**

Note: An asterisk (*) indicates an exception to the rule.

Vocabulary

1. **auxiliary** (ôg·zĭl′yə·rē), adj. **additional, helping**
   A helping verb is sometimes called an ***auxiliary*** verb.

2. **lethal** (lē′thəl), adj. **deadly**
   The insecticide sprinkled on the anthill was ***lethal*** to the fire ants.

3. **munitions** (myo͞o·nĭsh′əns), n. **war materials, such as weapons**
   Many factories during WWII produced ***munitions.***

4. **negligent** (nĕg′lĭ·jənt), adj. **habitually inattentive, careless, irresponsible**
   The ***negligent*** nurse gave the wrong medication to her patient.

5. **perpendicular** (pûr′pən·dĭk′yə·lər), adj. **vertical, precipitous, steep**
   The climbers looked up the ***perpendicular*** face of the cliff.

6. **profound** (prə·found′), adj. **intellectually deep**
   The ***profound*** truth of Scripture always amazes me.

7. **reliance** (rĭ·lī′əns), n. **trust, confidence, dependence**
   The founders of our country went forward with firm ***reliance*** on Almighty God.

8. **reminisce** (rĕm′ə·nĭs′), v. **recall, remember, recollect**
   Mr. Crona and Mr. Leland, two retired army colonels, often ***reminisce*** about World War II.

9. **wax** (wăks), v. **grow**
   And because iniquity shall abound, the love of many shall ***wax*** cold. *—Matt. 24:12*

10. **wistful** (wĭst′fəl), adj. **mournfully longing, yearning**
    The child cast a ***wistful*** glance at the toy in the shop window.

Exercises

A *From vocabulary list 5, choose the word that best completes each sentence. (Note: You may have to change the tense or form of the word.)*

1. An author in his memoirs will ________________ about the influence of past relationships.
2. It is helpful to have a(n) ________________ power source after a hurricane.
3. Proverbs shows Solomon's ________________ insight into human character.
4. With ________________ eyes, the young bride watched her husband sail away to war.
5. The soldier was told to obtain more ________________ for his company.
6. Legally, a manager can be considered ________________ if he does not protect his employees from a known hazard.
7. Some harmless-looking mushrooms are ________________ because they contain poison.
8. Humanism exists wherever man quits his ________________ on God and places all his confidence in human beings.
9. At Niagara, we gazed in awe at the ________________ fall of water.
10. Rich gifts ________________ poor when givers prove unkind. *—Shakespeare*

List 5

B *Write the vocabulary word from list 5 that is most nearly a* ***synonym*** *of the italicized expression.*

________________ 1. Absence makes the heart *grow* fonder. *—Thomas Haynes Bayly*

________________ 2. The rabies virus usually proves *fatal* to the carrier.

________________ 3. Jonathan Edwards had a *brilliant* ability to make complex ideas simple.

________________ 4. The *supplemental* aid came too late to be truly effective.

________________ 5. The immigrant's *desirous* countenance revealed his thoughts of his beloved country.

________________ 6. Family reunions are a good time to *remember.*

________________ 7. A man is justified by *faith* without the deeds of the law. *—Rom. 3:28*

LIST 6

Spelling

Words illustrating rule 1
(See page 4.)

1 **aggrieved**
2 **brigadier**
3 **cashier**
4 **chandelier**
5 **deign**
6 **either***
7 **grief**
8 **handkerchief**
9 **height***
10 **heinous**
11 **heir**
12 **hygiene**
13 **lien**
14 **pierce**
15 **reprieve**
16 **seizure***
17 **shriek**
18 **surveillance**
19 **transient**
20 **weigh**

Note: An asterisk (*) indicates an exception to the rule.

Vocabulary

1. **adjacent** (ə·jā′sənt), adj. **adjoining**
   The ***adjacent*** buildings were not damaged in the fire.

2. **appall** (ə·pôl′), v. **dismay, frighten, horrify**
   Sin of any kind should ***appall*** a Christian.

3. **despotic** (dĕs·pŏt′ĭk), adj. **absolute, arbitrary, tyrannical**
   Many Christians were put to death by the ***despotic*** emperor Nero.

4. **empower** (ĕm·pou′ər), v. **authorize, enable, permit**
   He sought a power of attorney, which would ***empower*** him to act on his father's behalf.

5. **incoherent** (ĭn′kō·hîr′ənt), adj. **illogical, rambling, disjointed**
   His speech was so ***incoherent*** that we could not understand what he was saying.

6. **incredulous** (ĭn·krĕj′ə·ləs), adj. **doubtful, skeptical, unbelieving**
   After Christ had risen from the dead, Thomas remained ***incredulous*** until he could see Christ for himself and touch Him.

7. **luminous** (lo͞o′mə·nəs), adj. **bright, glowing**
   As the night thickened, the huge fires became more and more ***luminous.***

8. **sophistication** (sə·fĭs′tə·kā′shən), n. **refinement, cultivated tastes, cosmopolitan qualities**
   She has a level of ***sophistication*** unexpected in a teenager.

9. **shimmer** (shĭm′ər), v. **shine with a faint, flickering light**
   I like to watch the home lights ***shimmer*** across the still lake at night.

10. **teem** (tēm), v. **abound, swarm**
    Many streams in the Appalachian Mountains ***teem*** with trout.

Exercises

A *From vocabulary list 6, choose the word that best completes each sentence. (Note: You may have to change the tense or form of the word.)*

1. Traveling extensively in Europe can develop one's ____________________ .
2. The evolutionist's ____________________ attitude toward Creation changed when he became a Christian.
3. The bride's satin gown ____________________ in the candlelight.
4. The new warehouse will be ____________________ to the ones along the pier.
5. Ivan the Terrible, a cruel and ____________________ czar, spread alarm throughout Russia.
6. The child's words were ____________________ as she babbled excitedly.
7. The threats of the giant Goliath ____________________ the entire army of Israel.
8. Many clocks have ____________________ dials that are visible in the dark.
9. The Supreme Court has been ____________________ to interpret the Constitution.

List 6

B *Circle the word that is most nearly a* ***synonym*** *of the italicized vocabulary word in the introductory phrase.*

1. muttering *incoherent* sentences
   (a) unpersuasive (b) confused (c) oppressive (d) profound
2. Communism, that most *despotic* system of government
   (a) ungracious (b) insolent (c) blasphemous (d) totalitarian
3. when airports *teem* with people
   (a) expand (b) dispense (c) overflow (d) protrude
4. a *luminous* sea creature
   (a) shining (b) luxurious (c) mobile (d) slimy
5. *appalled* by the crash
   (a) stimulated (b) terrified (c) intrigued (d) comforted
6. *empowered* to appoint a successor
   (a) employed (b) admonished (c) allowed (d) forbidden
7. a wide-eyed, *incredulous* gaze
   (a) dutiful (b) suspicious (c) nonchalant (d) unresponsive

LIST 7

Spelling

Words illustrating rule 2 (See page 4.)

1 **accustomed**
2 **bidding**
3 **canceled**
4 **caroling**
5 **deterring**
6 **disgusted**
7 **engineering**
8 **gagging**
9 **greeting**
10 **imperiled**
11 **incurred**
12 **propeller**
13 **regretting**
14 **skipped**
15 **snipping**
16 **straighten**
17 **submitting**
18 **traveler**
19 **whipping**
20 **zealous**

Vocabulary

1. **anecdote** (ăn′ĭk·dōt), n. **brief story, narrative**
   Grandfather's favorite ***anecdote*** was about how he and my grandmother first met.

2. **consensus** (kən·sĕn′səs), n. **agreement reached by a group**
   The board came to a ***consensus*** on the decision.

3. **delectable** (dĭ·lĕk′tə·bəl), adj. **delightful, delicious**
   Uncle Ray prepared us a most ***delectable*** trout dinner.

4. **delinquent** (dĭ·lĭng′kwənt), adj. **guilty of offense, neglectful, overdue**
   I cleared my ***delinquent*** account when I paid my library fine.

5. **domain** (dō·mān′), n. **field, sphere, province**
   If anything in the ***domain*** of science conflicts with God's Word, there is something wrong with the science.

6. **epitaph** (ĕp′ĭ·tăf), n. **tombstone inscription**
   John Keats's ***epitaph*** reads, "Here lies one whose name was writ in water."

7. **exhilarating** (ĭg·zĭl′ə·rāt′ĭng), adj. **refreshing, invigorating, stimulating**
   The cold morning made for an ***exhilarating*** walk.

8. **feasible** (fē′zə·bəl), adj. **possible, logical**
   Is ethanol a ***feasible*** alternative to gasoline?

9. **grievance** (grē′vəns), n. **complaint, injustice**
   My ***grievance*** stems from being unfairly fired from my job.

10. **maxim** (măk′sĭm), n. **adage, proverb, saying**
    We have reversed the wise ***maxim*** of Theodore Roosevelt, "Speak softly and carry a big stick." *—James P. Warburg*

Exercises

A *From vocabulary list 7, choose the word that best completes each sentence. (Note: You may have to change the tense or form of the word.)*

1. With the scholarship, attending college is ____________________ .
2. The IRS charges large fines for ____________________ taxes.
3. Many companies desire to correct their customers' legitimate ____________________ .
4. Mixing ____________________ and historical details, the author vividly described his famous father.
5. It is helpful when resolving a conflict to come to a ____________________ on the solution.
6. Alex likes to visit Grandmother, because she always bakes a variety of ____________________ cookies.
7. Reading the Psalms can be ____________________ to my spirit.
8. The verse "For to me to live is Christ, and to die is gain" is a good ____________________ for a Christian.
9. Those who try to live only in the ____________________ of the physical are only half alive.
10. "An ounce of prevention is worth a pound of cure" is one of Benjamin Franklin's many ____________________ .

List 7

B *Write the vocabulary word from list 7 that is most nearly a* ***synonym*** *of the word at the left.*

1. luscious ____________________	5. tale ____________________
2. motto ____________________	6. territory ____________________
3. energizing ____________________	7. wrong ____________________
4. majority opinion ____________________	8. dereliction of duty ____________________

Review Exercises

Lists 1–7

A

In the following sentences, circle the vocabulary word in parentheses that best completes the meaning.

1. While airing his (grievances, guile), the councilman objected to the city's (meditating, instituting) any new taxes before they had been (scrutinized, lacerated).

2. On January 12, 1991, Congress (lamented, empowered) the President to order the United States armed forces to wage war on Iraq, the (domain, morale) of the (exhilarating, despotic) ruler Saddam Hussein.

3. (Steadfast, Lavish) in her decision not to (tolerate, yoke) any more disobedience, Mother (appalled, admonished) Christina to behave.

4. Benjamin Franklin's writings (wax, teem) with (tangible, profound) (maxims, epitaphs) like the following: "A penny saved is a penny earned."

5. The Venerable Bede, a (ludicrous, meticulous) scholar, (instituted, scrutinized) ancient documents as he wrote *Ecclesiastical History of the English People.*

B

After each pair of words, write either the word ***antonyms*** *or the word* ***synonyms*** *depending on whether the words are more nearly opposite or more nearly the same in meaning. Write your answer for each in the space provided.*

1. sumptuous, magnificent ____________________
2. honesty, guile ____________________
3. irrepressible, tractable ____________________
4. accumulate, acquire ____________________
5. peace offering, irritant ____________________
6. area, domain ____________________
7. shallow, profound ____________________
8. attentive, negligent ____________________

C

Match each vocabulary word with its definition.

_________ 1. soft leather used for cleaning

_________ 2. the condition of being unknown

_________ 3. habitually inattentive, careless, irresponsible

_________ 4. outward bearing or behavior

_________ 5. agreement reached by a group

_________ 6. cause of annoyance

_________ 7. refreshing, invigorating, stimulating

_________ 8. illogical, rambling, disjointed

_________ 9. carefully, cautiously

_________ 10. rend, tear, mangle

_________ 11. claiming to be worthy of distinction, showy

_________ 12. adjoining

_________ 13. worsen, intensify

_________ 14. authorize, enable, permit

_________ 15. bright, glowing

_________ 16. grow

_________ 17. move or develop faster

_________ 18. additional, helping

_________ 19. refinement, cultivated tastes, cosmopolitan qualities

_________ 20. tombstone inscription

A. accelerate
B. adjacent
C. aggravate
D. auxiliary
E. chamois
F. consensus
G. demeanor
H. empower
I. epitaph
J. exhilarating
K. gingerly
L. guile
M. incoherent
N. irritant
O. lacerate
P. lethal
Q. luminous
R. morale
S. negligent
T. obscurity
U. pretentious
V. sophistication
W. wax

Spelling

Words illustrating rule 3 (See page 5.)

1 **accompanied**
2 **apologies**
3 **carrier**
4 **chimneys**
5 **decoys**
6 **denied**
7 **emergencies**
8 **hatcheries**
9 **identifying**
10 **industries**
11 **inquiries**
12 **likelihood**
13 **luxurious**
14 **modifying**
15 **nullified**
16 **salaries**
17 **trolleys**
18 **valleys**
19 **various**
20 **worrying**

Vocabulary

1. **certitude** (sûr′tĭ·to͞od), n. **assurance, sureness, conviction**

   I have such ***certitude*** in God that my faith cannot be shaken.

2. **chivalry** (shĭv′əl·rē), n. **courtesy, honorableness, bravery**

   Chivalry still lives in those who defend truth.
   —Kenelm Digby

3. **indispensable** (ĭn′dĭ·spĕn′sə·bəl), adj. **necessary, essential**

   Bible reading is ***indispensable*** for spiritual growth.

4. **indulgent** (ĭn·dŭl′jənt), adj. **lenient, tolerant, pampering**

   To be ***indulgent*** with yourself is to greatly decrease your chances of success in life.

5. **lateral** (lăt′ər·əl), adj. **sideways**

   The ***lateral*** movements of the crab surprised the youngster.

6. **pliable** (plī′ə·bəl), adj. **easily bent, flexible**

   Clay will remain ***pliable*** while it is moist.

7. **scour** (skour), v. **clean by scrubbing**

   Please ***scour*** the tub on Saturday.

8. **squall** (skwôl), n. **violent windstorm**

   A ***squall*** is often accompanied by rain or snow.

9. **subordinate** (sə·bôr′dn·ĭt), adj. **inferior in rank or authority, secondary**

   The receptionist is ***subordinate*** to the manager.

10. **veneer** (və·nēr′), n. **thin layer over a less valuable material**

    The dining table has a walnut ***veneer.***

Exercises

A *From vocabulary list 8, choose the word that best completes each sentence. (Note: You may have to change the tense or form of the word.)*

1. The blacksmith heated the iron until it was ____________________ and then pounded it into an andiron.
2. When a ____________________ blew in, the ship headed for port.
3. George treated all women with ____________________, just as he would want his mother to be treated.
4. Jacob realizes that athletics should be ____________________ to academics.
5. The truths of the Bible must be held with absolute ____________________.
6. My grandmother always ____________________ the oven when she comes to visit.
7. The quarterback threw a ____________________ pass to his halfback near the sideline.
8. Grandparents are often ____________________ with their grandchildren.
9. Susan has become a(n) ____________________ member of the team.
10. Cheaper furniture will often use ____________________, rather than solid wood.

List 8

B *Write the vocabulary word from list 8 that is most nearly* ***opposite*** *in meaning to each of the following words.*

1. chief ____________________
2. calm ____________________
3. rigid ____________________
4. soil ____________________
5. rudeness ____________________
6. doubt ____________________
7. needless ____________________
8. strict ____________________

LIST 9

Spelling

Words illustrating rule 4 (See page 5.)

1 **acknowledgment***
2 **acquirable**
3 **advantageous***
4 **announcement**
5 **approximately**
6 **assurance**
7 **ceaseless**
8 **dazzling**
9 **desirable**
10 **fiercely**[1, 4]
11 **greasy**
12 **icy**
13 **ignorance**
14 **knowledgeable***
15 **legitimately**
16 **likable**
17 **maturing**
18 **mileage***
19 **receivable**[1, 4]
20 **rechargeable***

Note: A superscript number ([1, 2,] etc.) after a word indicates the spelling rule on page 3 which applies. An asterisk (*) indicates an exception to the rule.

Vocabulary

1. **expanse** (ĭk·spăns′), n. **widely extended area**

   The Almighty spake: Let there be lights high in the ***expanse*** of Heaven. —*Milton*

2. **foster** (fôs′tər), v. **encourage, promote, further**

   One should read books that ***foster*** pure and noble thoughts.

3. **goad** (gōd), v. **prod, spur, urge**

   My brother always needs someone to ***goad*** him into action.

4. **illiterate** (ĭl·lĭt′ər·ĭt), adj. **unable to read or write**

   Many high school graduates today are functionally ***illiterate.***

5. **intricacy** (ĭn′trĭ·kə·sē), n. **complexity**

   Because of the ***intricacy*** of its design, the pottery is very valuable.

6. **invulnerable** (ĭn·vŭl′nər·ə·bəl), adj. **uninjurable, unassailable, invincible**

   Achilles was ***invulnerable*** except in his heel.

7. **muster** (mŭs′tər), v. **call, summon, gather**

   An officer must sometimes ***muster*** his troops on short notice.

8. **predatory** (prĕd′ə·tôr′ē), adj. **preying, plundering, pillaging**

   The gray wolf, a ***predatory*** animal, feasts on sheep and cattle.

9. **turmoil** (tûr′moil), n. **great commotion, trouble, or confusion**

   The military coup caused great ***turmoil.***

10. **unwieldy** (ŭn·wēl′dē), adj. **awkward, clumsy, unmanageable**

    The young squire could hardly carry the ***unwieldy*** sword.

Exercises

A *From vocabulary list 9, choose the word that best completes each sentence. (Note: You may have to change the tense or form of the word.)*

1. Grandmother could not move the ____________________ trunk.
2. Desiring to be ____________________, an athlete follows a strenuous regime.
3. Our church ____________________ the preaching of the gospel through missions.
4. Delilah ____________________ Samson into disclosing the secret of his strength.
5. Many ____________________ animals live in the jungles of Africa.
6. A sergeant usually will ____________________ his new recruits for roll call as soon as they arrive on base.
7. I had much inner ____________________ about the decision until I asked God for direction.
8. The ____________________ of the case required the skills of Sherlock Holmes.
9. An ____________________ person does not read and write.
10. We gazed at the magnificent ____________________ of the Grand Canyon.

B *Circle the word that is most nearly a* ***synonym*** *of the vocabulary word at the left.*

1. invulnerable	(a) doubtful	(b) reluctant	(c) amazing	(d) impenetrable
2. unwieldy	(a) manageable	(b) cumbersome	(c) stubborn	(d) steep
3. foster	(a) advance	(b) aggravate	(c) tolerate	(d) institute
4. expanse	(a) territory	(b) overflow	(c) brake	(d) portrayal
5. muster	(a) inspire	(b) support	(c) assemble	(d) disperse
6. goad	(a) push	(b) appall	(c) satiate	(d) yoke
7. illiterate	(a) ignorant	(b) incoherent	(c) educated	(d) devious
8. predatory	(a) extravagant	(b) devouring	(c) devious	(d) delicious
9. intricacy	(a) obscurity	(b) perspective	(c) plainness	(d) difficulty
10. turmoil	(a) encouragement	(b) lawlessness	(c) upheaval	(d) order

LIST 10

Spelling

Words ending in *-ence, -ance; -ency, -ancy; -ent, -ant* (Apply "Keys to Good Spelling" number 4, page 6.)

1 **absence**
2 **acquaintance**
3 **apparent**
4 **assistance**
5 **attendance**
6 **buoyancy**
7 **competent**
8 **constancy**
9 **despondency**
10 **disappearance**
11 **excellent**
12 **existence**
13 **incandescence**
14 **insurance**
15 **intelligence**
16 **pleasant**
17 **resistance**
18 **tendency**
19 **vagrancy**
20 **warrant**

Vocabulary

1. **baffle** (băf′əl), v. **frustrate, confound, foil**
   Our Lord can confuse His enemies and completely ***baffle*** their efforts.
2. **deface** (dĭ·fās′), v. **disfigure, mar, damage**
   It is illegal to ***deface*** our American currency.
3. **futile** (fyo͞o′tĭl), adj. **vain, useless, unavailing**
   All attempts to destroy the Jews have been ***futile*** because God has always intervened.
4. **harbor** (här′bər), v. **protect, secure, shelter**
   It is illegal to ***harbor*** criminals.
5. **labored** (lā′bərd), adj. **forced, strained, unnatural**
   Our breathing became ***labored*** as we hiked up the mountain.
6. **levee** (lĕv′ē), n. **embankment, dike, dam**
   The ***levee*** along the river broke in a recent storm.
7. **mantle** (măn′tl), n. **loose, sleeveless coat**
   Elisha took up Elijah's ***mantle*** after Elijah was caught up into heaven.
8. **mauve** (mōv), n. **light reddish or grayish purple**
   The sunset painted the sky with muted shades of ***mauve.***
9. **pomp** (pŏmp), n. **splendor and magnificence**
   The prince was married with all the ***pomp*** that royalty could afford.
10. **veranda** (və·răn′də), n. **open porch**
    Potted geraniums lined the ***veranda*** of the colonial home.

Exercises

A *From vocabulary list 10, choose the word that best completes each sentence. (Note: You may have to change the tense or form of the word.)*

1. ______________________ is a popular color for dresses this spring.
2. Rahab was spared by Joshua because she ______________________ the Israelite spies.
3. From the ______________________ , I could watch the children.
4. On June 2, 1953, many enjoyed the ______________________ of Queen Elizabeth II's coronation.
5. The brain continues to ______________________ medical researchers.
6. The landlord did not allow pets because they can ______________________ floorings.
7. Then Job arose, and rent his ______________________ , and shaved his head, and fell down upon the ground, and worshipped. *—Job 1:20*
8. The doctors' efforts to save the wounded officer were ______________________ .
9. The pony ______________________ under its heavy load.
10. One of the world's largest ______________________ was built along the Nile River.

List
10

B *Circle the word that is most nearly an* ***antonym*** *of the italicized word in the expression at the left.*

1. *futile* opposition
   (a) vain (b) effective (c) fruitless (d) idle
2. to *harbor* stray pets
   (a) summon (b) ignore (c) satisfy (d) endanger
3. *labored* attempt
   (a) reluctant (b) lenient (c) easy (d) concise
4. to *deface* private property
   (a) restore (b) confound (c) permit (d) mangle
5. *baffle* the reporters
   (a) lacerate (b) summon (c) warn (d) assist
6. *pomp* associated with nobility
   (a) gallantry (b) informality (c) grandeur (d) rudeness

LIST 11

Spelling

Words ending in *-er, -or* and *-able, -ible* (Apply "Keys to Good Spelling" number 4, page 6.)

1 **accessible**
2 **available**
3 **cylinder**
4 **debtor**
5 **denominator**
6 **eligible**
7 **excitable**[4]
8 **factor**
9 **governor**
10 **indispensable**
11 **informer**
12 **junior**
13 **labor**
14 **lacquer**
15 **monitor**
16 **noticeable**[4*]
17 **philosopher**
18 **professor**
19 **superior**
20 **tailor**

Note: A superscript number ([1, 2,] etc.) after a word indicates the spelling rule on pages 4–5 which applies. An asterisk (*) indicates an exception to the rule.

Vocabulary

1. **aptitude** (ăp′tĭ·to͞od), n. **natural ability, talent**
   Thomas Edison had a great ***aptitude*** for mechanical inventions.

2. **discern** (dĭ·sûrn′), v. **distinguish, perceive, recognize**
   Can you ***discern*** right from wrong?

3. **impromptu** (ĭm·prŏmp′to͞o), adj. **unrehearsed, unprepared**
   Giving an ***impromptu*** speech reveals one's knowledge of a subject.

4. **loiter** (loi′tər), v. **aimlessly or idly linger, dawdle**
   Students should not ***loiter*** in the hallways during class.

5. **moor** (mo͞or), v. **anchor, secure**
   We often ***moor*** our boat in the middle of the lake to swim.

6. **perpetual** (pər·pĕt′ū·əl), adj. **lasting, permanent**
   The earth revolves in ***perpetual*** motion.

7. **phenomenon** (fĭ·nŏm′ə·nŏn), n. **wonder, extremely unusual occurrence**
   Christ spoke of the ***phenomenon*** of stars falling from heaven.

8. **rendezvous** (rän′dā·vo͞o), n. **meeting place**
   Camp David is often a ***rendezvous*** for U.S. leaders.

9. **reservoir** (rĕz′ər·vwär′), n. **place for storing liquids**
   My car's oil ***reservoir*** holds five quarts.

10. **unceremoniously** (ŭn·sĕr′ə·mō′nē·əs·lē), adv. **abruptly, informally, rudely**
    Timothy threw down his fork and ***unceremoniously*** left the dinner table.

Exercises

A *From vocabulary list 11, choose the word that best completes each sentence. (Note: You may have to change the tense or form of the word.)*

1. Come, and let us join ourselves to the Lord in a ____________________ covenant that shall not be forgotten. *—Jer. 50:5*
2. Because of its political neutrality, Switzerland is often chosen as a ____________________ for foreign leaders and diplomats.
3. Susan left me ____________________ outside the mall while she shopped inside.
4. Unlike many other mammals, monkeys can see in depth and ____________________ colors.
5. Beethoven's ____________________ for composing music was astounding.
6. Many ____________________ are used to store and supply water to cities.
7. Sometimes a speaker's ____________________ lines are prompted by a recent event.
8. Without much warning, Timothy was ____________________ promoted to manager.
9. While in Catalina Island, we had to ____________________ our boat outside the harbor.
10. The Israelites' walking across the Red Sea on dry ground was an amazing ____________________ .

List 11

B *To complete this puzzle, choose the word from list 11 that is most likely to be associated with each clue below. Put each answer in the squares beginning with the number of the clue.*

1. respond curtly
2. "Meet you there!"
3. unrehearsed performance
4. continuing without interruption
5. taking to water like a duck
6. the manna from heaven
7. to recognize the difference between diamonds and cut glass
8. lag behind to window shop
9. secure with anchors
10. often created by dams

Spelling

Homophones (See "Keys to Good Spelling" number 5, page 7.)

1 **cache** (hiding place)
2 **cash** (money)
3 **cents** (money)
4 **sense** (function)
5 **earn** (make money)
6 **urn** (a vase)
7 **forth** (direction)
8 **fourth** (number)
9 **miner** (worker)
10 **minor** (underage)
11 **muscle** (tissue)
12 **mussel** (seafood)
13 **peace** (harmony)
14 **piece** (a part)
15 **plain** (level area)
16 **plane** (a tool)
17 **rite** (ceremony)
18 **write** (use a pen)
19 **you'll** ("you will")
20 **Yule** (Christmas)

Vocabulary

1. **anticipation** (ăn·tĭs′ə·pā′shən), n. **expectation**
   Eric looked forward with eager ***anticipation*** to his new car.

2. **bravado** (brə·vä′dō), n. **show of courage or boldness**
   Herman's ***bravado*** disappeared when he came face to face with a skunk in the cave.

3. **galvanize** (găl′və·nīz), v. **stimulate or motivate to action**
   Some believe that tax cuts will ***galvanize*** more life into the stock market.

4. **gaudy** (gôd′ē), adj. **tastelessly fine, showy**
   The ***gaudy*** hat had peacock feathers and scarlet ribbons.

5. **hoary** (hōr′ē), adj. **white or gray-haired**
   The man's ***hoary*** head bobbed forward as he slept.

6. **liquidate** (lĭk′wĭ·dāt), v. **settle debts by selling off assets**
   The furniture store has to ***liquidate*** its inventory because it is closing.

7. **plenteous** (plĕn′tē·əs), adj. **abundant, plentiful**
   The Lord is merciful and gracious, slow to anger, and ***plenteous*** in mercy. *—Psa. 103:8*

8. **proclaim** (prō·klām′), v. **announce publicly, declare**
   Proclaim the good news of the gospel.

9. **turbulent** (tûr′byə·lənt), adj. **violently agitated or disturbed**
   The path of duty often leads through ***turbulent*** waters.

10. **valiant** (văl′yənt), adj. **brave, courageous**
    The ***valiant*** soldier stood his watch.

Exercises

A *From vocabulary list 12, choose the word that best completes each sentence. (Note: You may have to change the tense or form of the word.)*

1. The young man ______________________ to all his new engagement.
2. The costume jewelry was too ______________________ to wear with the elegant dress.
3. Children may show ______________________ when their friends are near, but when alone, their courage often fails.
4. When the business went bankrupt, it ______________________ its inventory to settle its debts.
5. The ______________________ head is a crown of glory, if it be found in the way of righteousness. *—Prov. 16:31*
6. With great ______________________ they waited to hear who had won the World Series.
7. He made a ______________________ attempt to rescue the child.
8. The airplane encountered ______________________ air currents.
9. Successful businessmen can ______________________ others into action.
10. The Lord promised the Israelites that if they would hearken to His voice He would make them "______________________ in goods" and productive in childbearing.

List 12

B *Write the vocabulary word from list 12 that is most nearly a* ***synonym*** *of the italicized word.*

______________________ 1. The *garish* hues of the large floral print were startlingly bright.

______________________ 2. This year's crop yielded a *bountiful* harvest.

______________________ 3. The *prospect* of a quick victory boosted the army's morale.

______________________ 4. Thomas Carlyle said that sincerity is a *heroic* quality.

______________________ 5. The bully's *boasting* crumbled into dread when he saw the principal.

______________________ 6. Sometimes it is difficult to *stir* people into supporting worthy causes.

______________________ 7. Paul Revere *published* the approach of the British.

______________________ 8. The *tumultuous* winds laid flat the cornstalks.

Spelling

Homophones (See "Keys to Good Spelling" number 5, page 7.)

1 **berth** (place to sleep)
2 **birth** (being born)
3 **canvas** (cloth)
4 **canvass** (survey)
5 **censer** (incense vessel)
6 **censor** (cut out)
7 **chord** (musical tones)
8 **cord** (small rope)
9 **coarse** (rough)
10 **course** (direction)
11 **complement** (completes)
12 **compliment** (praise)
13 **core** (center)
14 **corps** (military group)
15 **doe** (female deer)
16 **dough** (flour paste)
17 **faint** (swoon)
18 **feint** (fake attack)
19 **tern** (sea bird)
20 **turn** (change direction)

Vocabulary

1. **brink** (brĭngk), n. **edge, border, verge**
   Standing at the ***brink*** of the Grand Canyon, we could see the Colorado River coursing below.

2. **careen** (kə·rēn′), v. **list, sway, lurch**
   Pulled by spooked horses, the buckboard ***careened*** over the rough terrain.

3. **eddy** (ĕd′ē), n. **circular current, whirlpool**
   Our raft was thrown onto the rocks by a wild ***eddy.***

4. **furbish** (fûr′bĭsh), v. **polish, burnish, shine**
   The antique dealer ***furbished*** the carved oak chest.

5. **flammable** (flăm′ə·bəl), adj. **easily burnable**
   Keep ***flammable*** materials away from open flames.

6. **jot** (jŏt), n. **particle, whit, iota**
   Till heaven and earth pass, one ***jot*** or one tittle shall in no wise pass from the law, till all be fulfilled. *—Matt. 5:18*

7. **liable** (lī′ə·bəl), adj. **legally responsible**
   Because the man was found guilty, he was ***liable*** for the cost of the damage.

8. **overwrought** (ō′vər·rôt′), adj. **extremely nervous or agitated**
   The ***overwrought*** child could not stop crying.

9. **prudent** (pro͞od′nt), adj. **wise, sensible, judicious**
   It is ***prudent*** to listen to instruction.

10. **refrain** (rĭ·frān′), v. **forgo, forbear, abstain**
    Should we ask Dad to ***refrain*** from singing in the shower?

Exercises

A *From vocabulary list 13, choose the word that best completes each sentence. (Note: You may have to change the tense or form of the word.)*

1. Sir John Falstaff judged it more ________________ to play dead than to fight.
2. In heavy seas, the craft ________________ and shook.
3. The knights ________________ their swords as they readied for battle.
4. Never use gasoline to start a fire because it is highly ________________.
5. A Spirit-filled Christian will ________________ from saying unkind things.
6. The strong ________________ in the stream made swimming dangerous.
7. "Not a ________________ of that testimony is true!" exclaimed the defendant.
8. A store may be ________________ for damages if someone is injured on its property.
9. Moses' mother placed her son in an ark of bulrushes by the river's ________________.
10. The hazardous conditions during Hurricane Katrina caused me to feel ________________.

B *Give the letter of the word at the right that is most nearly an **antonym** of each vocabulary word at the left.*

________	1. jot	A. calm
________	2. flammable	B. stay upright
________	3. overwrought	C. deface
________	4. prudent	D. uncivil
________	5. furbish	E. interior
________	6. careen	F. whole
________	7. refrain	G. indulge
________	8. brink	H. blithe
		I. fireproof
		J. anger
		K. foolish

LIST 14

Spelling

"Seed" Words and Other Commonly Misspelled Words

1 **accede**†
2 **annually**
3 **antecede**†
4 **boundary**
5 **concede**†
6 **disciple**
7 **evidently**
8 **exceed**†
9 **finally**
10 **generally**
11 **intercede**†
12 **occasion**
13 **practice**
14 **precede**†
15 **proceed**
16 **recede**†
17 **secede**†
18 **succeed**†
19 **supersede**†
20 **surrounded**

†Super**sede** is the only verb in English that ends in *-sede.* Ex**ceed,** pro**ceed,** and suc**ceed** are the only verbs that end in *-ceed.* All the other endings that have a "seed" sound are spelled *-cede.*

Vocabulary

1. **complaisant** (kəm·plā′sənt), adj. **obliging, agreeable, willing to please**
   Loyal and ***complaisant,*** Mother agreed to chaperone our field trip.

2. **deficiency** (dĭ·fĭsh′ən·sē), n. **inadequacy, shortcoming**
   You can make up for a ***deficiency*** in ability through hard work.

3. **disfigure** (dĭs·fĭg′yər), v. **ruin the appearance of**
   Injuries from a car accident can permanently ***disfigure*** one.

4. **entrench** (ĕn·trĕnch′), v. **dig in, fortify, establish**
   They will ***entrench*** themselves along a ridge opposite the enemy.

5. **excavate** (ĕks′kə·vāt′), v. **scoop or hollow out**
   A bulldozer is used to ***excavate*** building sites.

6. **execute** (ĕk′sĭ·kyo͞ot′), v. **do, carry out, accomplish**
   We must ***execute*** our game plan perfectly to win.

7. **posterity** (pŏs·tĕr′ĭ·tē), n. **succeeding generations, descendants**
   The Youth of a Nation are the trustees of ***Posterity.*** *—Benjamin Disraeli*

8. **procure** (prō·kyo͝or′), v. **get, acquire**
   Rare books are often impossible to ***procure.***

9. **propriety** (prə·prī′ĭ·tē), n. **correctness of behavior or morals**
   The Bible says that fools scoff at ***propriety.*** *—Prov. 14:9*

10. **unrelenting** (ŭn′rĭ·lĕn′tĭng), adj. **not slackening**
    The ***unrelenting*** bombing destroyed most of the village.

Exercises

A *From vocabulary list 14, choose the word that best completes each sentence. (Note: You may have to change the tense or form of the word.)*

1. The vandal ______________________ the priceless piece of art.
2. A Christian should not be so ______________________ that he compromises Scriptural principles.
3. Thus speaketh the Lord of hosts, saying, ______________________ true judgment, and shew mercy and compassions every man to his brother. *—Zech. 7:9*
4. One generation should not leave its problems for ______________________ to solve.
5. The ______________________ fury of the storm frightened the children.
6. He that reads and grows no wiser seldom suspects his own ______________________ . *—Samuel Johnson*
7. While the construction workers were ______________________ , they discovered an old Indian burial ground.
8. Unfortunately, many critics belittle the ______________________ of Victorian England.
9. He is so ______________________ in his liberalism that it seems impossible to dislodge him.
10. His task was to ______________________ the supplies needed by his unit.

B *Write the vocabulary word from list 14 that is most nearly a* ***synonym*** *of each of the following words.*

1. lack ______________________
2. solidify ______________________
3. unyielding ______________________
4. decency ______________________
5. flexible ______________________
6. obtain ______________________
7. perform ______________________
8. mar ______________________
9. offspring ______________________
10. dredge ______________________

Review Exercises

Lists 1–14

A

Circle the word that is most nearly a ***synonym*** *of the italicized word in each expression.*

1. the ***sumptuous*** dinner at the emperor's palace
   (a) delectable (c) incredulous
   (b) lavish (d) ludicrous
2. a ***perpetual*** threat to the principles of democracy
   (a) perennial (c) perpendicular
   (b) tangible (d) subsequent
3. the ***morale*** of the Allied troops
   (a) demeanor (c) chivalry
   (b) self-confidence (d) pomp
4. the ***feasible*** choice of action
   (a) gaudy (c) reasonable
   (b) baffling (d) turbulent
5. to ***muster*** the soldiers for battle
   (a) entrench (c) collect
   (b) empower (d) galvanize

B

Circle the word that is most nearly an ***antonym*** *of the italicized word in each expression.*

1. Satan is full of ***guile.***
   (a) bravado (c) pomp
   (b) integrity (d) sullenness
2. full of ***praises***
   (a) certitude (c) integrity
   (b) grievances (d) valor
3. ***furbishing*** their new Jaguar
   (a) accelerating (c) scrutinizing
   (b) goading (d) tarnishing
4. ***crudeness*** of manners
   (a) certitude (c) intricacy
   (b) informality (d) propriety
5. the ***unwieldy*** lump of clay
   (a) gingerly (c) pliable
   (b) indispensible (d) tangible

C

Match each vocabulary word with its definition.

_________ 1. ruin the appearance of

_________ 2. careful, accurate

_________ 3. legally responsible

_________ 4. assumed and supposed, accused without proof

_________ 5. expectation

_________ 6. not slackening

_________ 7. wise, sensible, judicious

_________ 8. reluctant, hesitant, disinclined

_________ 9. frustrate, confound, foil

_________ 10. habitually inattentive, careless, irresponsible

_________ 11. unable to read or write

_________ 12. war materials, such as ammunition and weapons

_________ 13. encourage, promote, further

_________ 14. forgo, forebear, abstain

_________ 15. forced, strained, unnatural

_________ 16. worsen, intensify

_________ 17. thin layer over a less valuable material

_________ 18. obliging, agreeable, willing to please

_________ 19. unrehearsed, unprepared

_________ 20. do, carry out, accomplish

A. aggravate
B. alleged
C. anticipation
D. baffle
E. certitude
F. complaisant
G. disfigure
H. execute
I. foster
J. illiterate
K. impromptu
L. incredulous
M. labored
N. liable
O. loath
P. meticulous
Q. munitions
R. negligent
S. prudent
T. refrain
U. scour
V. unrelenting
W. veneer

LIST 15

Spelling

Commonly misspelled words

1 **accidentally**
2 **actually**
3 **apology**
4 **authority**
5 **basically**
6 **behavior**
7 **category**
8 **chronological**
9 **forty**
10 **hypocrisy**
11 **mysterious**[3]
12 **necessary**
13 **opportunity**
14 **original**
15 **particular**
16 **probably**
17 **psychology**
18 **thorough**
19 **undoubtedly**
20 **whole**

Note: A superscript number ([1, 2,] etc.) after a word indicates the spelling rule on pages 4–5 which applies.

Vocabulary

1. **allocate** (ăl′ə·kāt), v. **set apart, apportion, assign**
   They will ***allocate*** ten new computers for the library.

2. **connive** (kə·nīv′), v. **secretly plot to do wrong, scheme, conspire**
   Criminals sometimes ***connive*** with customs officials to smuggle illegal goods.

3. **dispatch** (dĭs·păch′), v. **send**
   The United States can ***dispatch*** a Patriot missile to intercept an enemy missile.

4. **embark** (ĕm·bärk′), v. **board a vessel or aircraft, set out**
   They will ***embark*** tomorrow for a tour of duty in Iraq.

5. **emit** (ĭ·mĭt′), v. **send forth**
   Under a load, diesel engines ***emit*** black smoke.

6. **inestimable** (ĭn·ĕs′tə·mə·bəl), adj. **incalculable, priceless**
   The wisdom that God alone can give is ***inestimable.***

7. **rapture** (răp′chər), n. **bliss, happiness, ecstasy**
   Rapture shone from the child's face as she opened her presents.

8. **reconcile** (rĕk′ən·sīl), v. **settle, resolve, harmonize**
   Did the feuding Hatfields and McCoys ever ***reconcile*** their differences?

9. **remorse** (rĭ·môrs′), n. **sorrow, grief, regret**
   It is better to refrain from sin than to live with ***remorse.***

10. **solicit** (sə·lĭs′ĭt), v. **ask, request**
    The company will ***solicit*** new business from overseas.

Exercises

A *From vocabulary list 15, choose the word that best completes each sentence. (Note: You may have to change the tense or form of the word.)*

1. Jacob ____________________ with his mother Rebekah to steal Esau's birthright.
2. Ultraviolet rays are ____________________ from the sun.
3. Leave there thy gift before the altar, and go thy way; first be ____________________ to thy brother, and then come and offer thy gift. *—Matt. 5:24*
4. On April 14, 1912, the Titanic ____________________ on a voyage of no return.
5. Judas felt such ____________________ for betraying the Lord that he hanged himself.
6. What a(n) ____________________ treasure we have in our parents!
7. The Presidential candidate ____________________ public support by promising not to raise taxes.
8. The king ____________________ messengers to deliver his proclamation to the royal townships.
9. God commanded the Israelites to ____________________ a tenth of their increase unto the Lord.
10. The young lady was filled with ____________________ when she saw the engagement ring.

List 15

B *Write the vocabulary word from list 15 that is most nearly a* ***synonym*** *of the italicized expression.*

____________________ 1. Nero, a cruel emperor, felt no *guilt* as he sentenced Christians to death.

____________________ 2. The Girl Scouts *asked* people to buy their cookies.

____________________ 3. I say unto you, that likewise *joy* shall be in heaven over one sinner that repenteth. . . . *—Luke 15:7*

____________________ 4. The Star of Africa diamond is a gem of *priceless* worth.

____________________ 5. Graduating from law school, Grace could now *start* her new career.

____________________ 6. An exploding star can *radiate* as much light as a galaxy.

____________________ 7. Several cities were *assigned* as places of refuge in the land of Israel.

____________________ 8. To *restore* oneself to an offended companion can require much humility.

____________________ 9. When a person dials 911 to report a fire, a telephone operator *forwards* the message to the nearest fire department.

LIST **16**

Spelling

Commonly misspelled words

1 **acquire**
2 **alleviate**
3 **amateur**
4 **bargain**
5 **beautiful**[3]
6 **commissioner**
7 **humorous**
8 **interference**[4]
9 **jealousy**
10 **laboratory**
11 **marriage**
12 **obstacle**
13 **optimism**
14 **referring**[2]
15 **relative**
16 **scene**
17 **sergeant**
18 **temperament**
19 **weather**
20 **whether**

Note: A superscript number ([1, 2,] etc.) after a word indicates the spelling rule on pages 4–5 which applies.

Vocabulary

1. **accentuate** (ăk·sĕn′chōō·āt′), v. **emphasize, stress**

   Being optimistic, Rebecca tends to ***accentuate*** the positive.

2. **allay** (ə·lā′), v. **relieve, calm, quiet**

   Mom used a night-light to ***allay*** Chloe's fear of the dark.

3. **aloof** (ə·lōōf′), adj. **physically and emotionally distant, reserved**

   The new student's shyness caused her to appear ***aloof.***

4. **brandish** (brăn′dĭsh), v. **shake or wave menacingly**

   King Arthur did ***brandish*** his sword often in battle.

5. **consumption** (kən·sŭmp′shən), n. **eating, devouring**

   Bob's rapid ***consumption*** of five hot tamales made him thirsty.

6. **domicile** (dŏm′ĭ·sīl), n. **home, residence, dwelling**

   The Brownings' ***domicile*** in Florence is now a museum.

7. **laden** (lād′n), adj. **burdened, weighed down**

   Come unto me, all ye that labour and are heavy ***laden,*** and I will give you rest. *—Matt. 11:28*

8. **meandering** (mē·ăn′dər·ĭng), adj. **winding, rambling, wandering**

   The ***meandering*** trail leads to the fishing hole.

9. **perilous** (pĕr′ə·ləs), adj. **dangerous, hazardous, risky**

   This know also, that in the last days ***perilous*** times shall come. *—2 Tim. 3:1*

10. **virtuous** (vûr′chōō·əs), adj. **moral, ethical, righteous**

    A ***virtuous*** woman is a crown to her husband. . . . *—Prov. 12:4*

Exercises

A *From vocabulary list 16, choose the word that best completes each sentence. (Note: You may have to change the tense or form of the word.)*

1. The wealthy executive bequeathed his ____________________ in Chevy Chase to his son.
2. The queen remained ____________________ from her subjects.
3. Who can find a ____________________ woman? for her price is far above rubies. *—Prov. 31:10*
4. We hiked along a ____________________ trail in the mountains.
5. Josh tried to ____________________ his puppy's fear during the storm.
6. The news warned us about the ____________________ weather.
7. The President's speech ____________________ the need to cut taxes.
8. Templeton deserved indigestion for his gluttonous ____________________ of the County Fair leftovers.
9. ____________________ with groceries, the lady struggled up the stairs.
10. The Three Musketeers ____________________ their gleaming swords.

B *Circle the word that is most nearly an* ***antonym*** *of the italicized word in each expression.*

1. The *consumption* of natural foods
   (a) allocation (b) solicitation (c) preservation (d) disposition
2. beside the *meandering* brook
   (a) invigorating (b) careening (c) teeming (d) unswerving
3. *aloof* manner
   (a) eloquent (b) exuberant (c) neighborly (d) standoffish
4. *brandishing* the dagger
   (a) furbishing (b) concealing (c) defacing (d) galvanizing
5. a *perilous* venture
   (a) safe (b) precarious (c) tangible (d) meticulous
6. to *allay* their agitation
   (a) appall (b) intensify (c) lament (d) alleviate
7. dangerously *laden* ships
   (a) loaded (b) steadfast (c) lacerated (d) unhampered
8. looked for *virtuous* companions
   (a) chaste (b) complaisant (c) sullen (d) immoral

Spelling

Commonly misspelled words

1 **anticipated**
2 **become**
3 **dealt**
4 **description**
5 **devastating**[4]
6 **discipline**
7 **discussion**
8 **embarrass**
9 **emphasize**
10 **exaggerate**
11 **hypocrite**
12 **interrupt**
13 **magazine**
14 **medieval**
15 **narrative**
16 **paralyzed**
17 **peculiar**
18 **realize**
19 **schedule**
20 **subtle**

Note: A superscript number ([1, 2,] etc.) after a word indicates the spelling rule on pages 4–5 which applies.

Vocabulary

1. **allied** (ə·līd′), adj. **joined, linked, affiliated**
   In World War II, the ***Allied*** forces defeated the Axis powers.

2. **apt** (ăpt), adj. **fit, suitable, appropriate**
   The speaker's ***apt*** remarks impressed the audience.

3. **incessant** (ĭn·sĕs′ənt), adj. **unceasing, continuous**
   The ***incessant*** bombing weakened the enemy.

4. **jargon** (jär′gŏn), n. **unintelligible language, lingo**
   Jargon prevents clear communication.

5. **jurisdiction** (jo͝or′ĭs·dĭk′shən), n. **right, power, authority**
   A court cannot rule where it has no ***jurisdiction.***

6. **kindred** (kĭn′drĕd), adj. **like, similar, agreeing**
   When two people share the same feelings, they have ***kindred*** spirits.

7. **minimize** (mĭn′ə·mīz), v. **diminish, belittle, lessen**
   Jesus would never ***minimize*** the exceeding sinfulness of sin.

8. **myriad** (mĭr′ĭ·əd), adj. **innumerable, countless**
   The ***myriad*** lights of New York City illuminated the night.

9. **precarious** (prĭ·kâr′ĭ·əs), adj. **uncertain, insecure**
   The truce led to only a ***precarious*** peace.

10. **venturesome** (vĕn′chər·səm), adj. **bold, inclined to take risks**
    The ***venturesome*** boy became lost while exploring the forest.

Exercises

A *From vocabulary list 17, choose the word that best completes each sentence. (Note: You may have to change the tense or form of the word.)*

1. Mark could not understand the legal ____________________ in the will.
2. The position of a king has often been ____________________ throughout history.
3. The ____________________ howling of the neighbor's dog was a nuisance.
4. ____________________ stars filled the night sky.
5. Any attempt to live exempt from God's ____________________ is to follow in the footsteps of Lucifer.
6. The ____________________ Amelia Earhart was the first woman to fly across the Atlantic Ocean.
7. The merchants at the mall were ____________________ in the effort to stop shoplifting.
8. Mr. Doyle meets periodically with ____________________ minds to discuss political issues.
9. A(n) ____________________ description of eternity is "the lifetime of God."
10. Cold compresses on a sprained ankle will help ____________________ the swelling.

B *Write the vocabulary word from list 17 that is most nearly a* ***synonym*** *of the italicized expression.*

List 17

____________________ 1. Some parts of the world have almost *continual* rain.

____________________ 2. The local police do not have *power* in the neighboring county.

____________________ 3. In all the play there is not one word *proper*, one player fitted. *—Shakespeare*

____________________ 4. It is not wise to *downplay* the achievements of others to build up your own esteem.

____________________ 5. The *peculiar, high-sounding language* of some journals can be difficult to understand.

____________________ 6. The stock market can be *risky* for investors.

____________________ 7. Yesterday we began studying about tornadoes and *associated* phenomena.

____________________ 8. Businessmen have to be *daring* to be successful.

____________________ 9. Our Lord Jesus Christ has provided us with *multitudinous* blessings.

____________________ 10. The *unified* countries worked together to fight terrorism.

LIST 18

Spelling

Commonly misspelled words

1 **acceptance**
2 **accommodate**
3 **attitude**
4 **condemn**
5 **decision**
6 **definitely**[4]
7 **encourage**
8 **enjoy**
9 **entrance**
10 **exercise**
11 **favorite**
12 **heroine**
13 **imagination**[4]
14 **immense**
15 **recognize**
16 **recommend**
17 **rhythm**
18 **suppress**
19 **tremendous**
20 **useful**[4]

Note: A superscript number ([1, 2,] etc.) after a word indicates the spelling rule on pages 4–5 which applies.

Vocabulary

1. **caustic** (kôs′tĭk), adj. **sharp, biting, sarcastic**
   Caustic remarks just create more conflict.

2. **comply** (kəm·plī), v. **obey, conform, submit**
   God alone can quiet the thunder and make the angry seas ***comply.***

3. **cordial** (kôr′jəl), adj. **friendly, warm, polite**
   The Williamses received a ***cordial*** welcome from their hostess.

4. **disposition** (dĭs′pə·zĭsh′ən), n. **typical personality, temperament, or mood**
   Emily's cheerful ***disposition*** encourages her classmates.

5. **knoll** (nōl), n. **small rounded hill**
   The Perrys' house, built on a ***knoll,*** is safe from floods.

6. **placid** (plăs′ĭd), adj. **calm, quiet, peaceful**
   The Porters enjoy canoeing on a ***placid*** lake.

7. **refinement** (rĭ·fīn′mənt), n. **fineness of taste, feeling, or thought**
   A lack of ***refinement*** is nothing to be proud of.

8. **smug** (smŭg), adj. **self-satisfied, self-complacent**
   A ***smug*** attitude often irritates others.

9. **stifle** (stī′fəl), v. **choke, smother, suppress**
   None are so narrow-minded as those who wish to ***stifle*** the free exercise of religion.

10. **whet** (hwĕt), v. **sharpen, stimulate, heighten**
    Good literature will ***whet*** your appetite for more.

Exercises

A *From vocabulary list 18, choose the word that best completes each sentence. (Note: You may have to change the tense or form of the word.)*

1. Humid summer nights often produce ________________ conditions in the South.
2. Visiting art museums can help develop one's ________________ .
3. Mr. Smith has been on ________________ terms with the Vice President for many years.
4. Worrying is a part of Sally's ________________ that she is working on with the Lord's help.
5. As Jesus was dying for the sins of the world, the religious leaders stood around making ________________ remarks.
6. The artist painted a ________________ scene of a doe and her fawn.
7. The aroma of sweet and sour pork really ________________ my appetite.
8. When the enemy did not ________________ with the cease-fire, their jets were shot down.
9. As a child, Laura Ingalls Wilder played on a grassy ________________ near Plum Creek.
10. Anne Shirley despised Josie Pye's ________________ expression.

List 18

B *Write the vocabulary word from list 18 that is most nearly a* ***synonym*** *of each expression.*

1. nature, tendency, makeup ________________
2. hone, stir, provoke ________________
3. dune, mound, hillock ________________
4. heartfelt, sociable, gracious ________________
5. suffocate, muffle ________________
6. conceited, proud, priggish ________________
7. relent, succumb, surrender ________________
8. serene, tranquil, undisturbed ________________
9. harsh, scathing, satiric ________________
10. polish, culture, elegance ________________

LIST 19

Spelling

Commonly misspelled words

1 **accomplish**
2 **accurate**
3 **against**
4 **analysis**
5 **appearance**
6 **basis**
7 **calendar**
8 **commercial**
9 **environment**
10 **foreigners**[1*]
11 **genius**
12 **hindrance**
13 **lengthening**
14 **manufacturers**
15 **oppose**
16 **privilege**
17 **separate**
18 **technique**
19 **vacuum**
20 **villain**

Note: A superscript number ([1, 2,] etc.) after a word indicates the spelling rule on pages 4–5 which applies. An asterisk (*) indicates an exception to the rule.

Vocabulary

1. **chronic** (krŏn′ĭk), adj. **persistent, long-lasting, continuing**
   She finally went to a doctor concerning her ***chronic*** headaches.

2. **emancipate** (ĭ·măn′sə·pāt′), v. **set free from bondage, liberate**
   One of the results of the Crimean War was Alexander II's decision to ***emancipate*** Russia's serfs in 1861.

3. **gaunt** (gônt), adj. **abnormally lean, haggard-looking**
   Surviving cholera, Henry was exhausted and ***gaunt.***

4. **grasping** (grăsp′ĭng), adj. **covetous, greedy**
   Charles Dickens described Scrooge as a ***grasping*** old sinner.

5. **murky** (mûr′kē), adj. **dim, dark, gloomy**
   Her hair became entangled in cobwebs in the ***murky*** root cellar.

6. **pertinent** (pûr′tə·nənt), adj. **relevant, related**
   Billy wrote to his state senator for ***pertinent*** information concerning several new bills.

7. **sheathe** (shēth), v. **enclose in a protective covering**
   Copper is sometimes used to ***sheathe*** a ship's hull.

8. **shoal** (shōl), n. **bank, reef, bar**
   The ship anchored a mile off shore to avoid the dangerous ***shoal.***

9. **vestige** (vĕs′tĭj), n. **trace, track, sign**
   There was not a ***vestige*** left of the ancient tribal customs.

10. **voracious** (vô·rā′shəs), adj. **ravenous, greedy, insatiable**
    Because of its high energy requirements, the tiny shrew is a ***voracious*** eater.

Exercises

A *From vocabulary list 19, choose the word that best completes each sentence. (Note: You may have to change the tense or form of the word.)*

1. ______________________ of extinct volcanoes exist in all the low countries on the western side of the Apennines. —*Davy*

2. The ______________________ brothers were angry when their father bequeathed his fortune to an orphanage.

3. Born into slavery in 1856, Booker T. Washington was ______________________ only to have to continue working in back-breaking jobs.

4. The knight ______________________ his sword after the battle.

5. God uses ______________________ illnesses to make Christians dependent on Him.

6. All information in a paragraph should be ______________________ to the topic sentence.

7. John Milton was such a ______________________ reader that he read many English, Latin, Greek, and Italian works.

8. The hostages were ______________________ and weak from months of captivity.

9. Many Scots believe that a monster lives in the ______________________ waters of Loch Ness.

10. "The Wreck of the *Hesperus*" describes how a ship was destroyed on a ______________________ named Norman's Woe.

List 19

B *Write the vocabulary word from list 19 that is most nearly **opposite** in meaning to each word.*

1. moderate ______________________
2. fleshy ______________________
3. expose ______________________
4. generous ______________________
5. enslave ______________________
6. irrelevant ______________________
7. infrequent ______________________
8. clear ______________________

LIST 20

Spelling

Commonly misspelled words

1 **apparatus**
2 **attire**
3 **breath**
4 **breathe**
5 **committees**
6 **confusion**
7 **disappointment**
8 **disillusioned**
9 **grammar**
10 **grammatically**
11 **hallelujah**
12 **influential**
13 **intellect**
14 **mischief**[1]
15 **numerous**
16 **performance**
17 **presence**
18 **procedure**
19 **source**
20 **tyranny**

Note: A superscript number ([1, 2,] etc.) after a word indicates the spelling rule on pages 4–5 which applies.

Vocabulary

1. **corpulent** (kôr′pyə·lənt), adj. **fleshy, fat, obese**
   Mrs. Byron . . . was a short and ***corpulent*** person and rolled considerably in her gait.
   —*Thomas Moore*

2. **disinterested** (dĭs·ĭn′tər·ĕs·tĕd), adj. **unbiased by personal interest, impartial**
   A judge must be ***disinterested*** to rule effectively.

3. **distraught** (dĭs·trôt′), adj. **deeply worried, distressed**
   The widow felt ***distraught*** over her unpaid bills.

4. **dividend** (dĭv′ĭ·dĕnd), n. **share, portion, gain**
   My aunt received a substantial ***dividend*** from her mutual fund.

5. **fetter** (fĕt′ər), v. **chain, shackle, confine**
   It is easier to ***fetter*** the body than the mind.

6. **grotesque** (grō·tĕsk′), adj. **bizarre, distorted, weird**
   Ancient buildings were often decorated with sculptures of ***grotesque*** monsters called gargoyles.

7. **minuscule** (mĭn′ə·skyo͞ol′), adj. **tiny, minute**
   The ***minuscule*** teacup poodle weighs up to 4 pounds.

8. **quandary** (kwŏn′də·rē), n. **state of extreme perplexity or uncertainty**
   We sat at the crossroads in a ***quandary*** about which road to take.

9. **superlative** (so͞o·pûr′lə·tĭv), adj. **supreme, unexcelled, unsurpassed**
   Chef Robard's chocolate cheesecake is ***superlative.***

10. **taut** (tôt), adj. **tightly drawn, tight, tense**
    The ropes holding the tent were as ***taut*** as bowstrings.

Exercises

A *From vocabulary list 20, choose the word that best completes each sentence. (Note: You may have to change the tense or form of the word.)*

1. Mrs. Petrovich was in a ______________________ about whether to call the police concerning a possible robbery.
2. A good referee will, of course, be ______________________, but one with a sense of humor can make a game more enjoyable.
3. Certificates of deposit provide fewer ______________________ than stocks.
4. The scrubby tree looked ______________________ and ghostly in the pale night sky.
5. Herod tried to stop Peter's preaching by ______________________ him.
6. The most ______________________ man in medical history weighed over 1,400 pounds.
7. The poetry reading had a ______________________ turnout because it was not advertised.
8. Read the Psalms for peace and comfort whenever you are feeling ______________________.
9. One of Michelangelo's ______________________ artworks is on the ceiling of the Sistine Chapel.

B *Write the vocabulary word from list 20 that is most nearly a* ***synonym*** *of the italicized word.*

______________________ 1. There are many *microscopic* organisms living in pond water.

______________________ 2. I now *tied* my horse to prevent his straying. —*Irving*

______________________ 3. He was short and *stout* and round about / And zealous as could be. —*W. S. Gilbert*

______________________ 4. The nervous bride was thrown into a *predicament* when she could not find her headpiece.

______________________ 5. Mr. Tisdale received an unusually large *share of profits* from his AT & T stock.

______________________ 6. John's parents were *anxious* when he did not come home on time.

______________________ 7. Judges try to make sure that only *neutral* jury members are selected.

______________________ 8. As the winds increased, the slack sails became *rigid.*

LIST 21

Spelling

Commonly misspelled words

1 **academically**
2 **appreciation**
3 **brilliant**
4 **bury**
5 **consequently**
6 **criticism**
7 **disease**
8 **divine**
9 **guarantee**
10 **handled**[4]
11 **involve**
12 **laborer**[2]
13 **morally**
14 **omit**
15 **persuade**
16 **propaganda**
17 **pursuit**
18 **shepherd**
19 **stepped**[2]
20 **woman**

Note: A superscript number ([1, 2,] etc.) after a word indicates the spelling rule on pages 4–5 which applies.

Vocabulary

1. **cumbersome** (kŭm′bər·səm), adj. **heavy, bulky, unwieldy**
   The hiker's ***cumbersome*** backpack made hiking harder.

2. **disheveled** (dĭ·shĕv′əld), adj. **disordered, disarranged, unkempt**
   Tumbling down the stairs left Mr. Slipdowne ***disheveled.***

3. **hysteria** (hĭs·tĕr′ĭ·ə), n. **unhealthy emotion**
   In 1938, a radio broadcast of a fictional Martian invasion caused great ***hysteria.***

4. **insolent** (ĭn′sə·lənt), adj. **disdainful, contemptuous, insulting**
   The ***insolent*** socialite insulted the waiter.

5. **mirage** (mĭ·räzh′), n. **a type of optical illusion**
   Although not an actual object, a ***mirage*** can be photographed because it consists of light rays.

6. **mortgage** (môr′gĭj), n. **a loan for buying property**
   I must get a ***mortgage*** if I want to buy this land.

7. **noxious** (nŏk′shəs), adj. **unwholesome, harmful**
   The ***noxious*** substance nicotine is used in liquid form as an insecticide.

8. **oblivious** (ə·blĭv′ē·əs), adj. **forgetful, no longer aware**
   Tamara was ***oblivious*** to the effect of her caustic words.

9. **palatial** (pə·lā′shəl), adj. **magnificent, luxurious, befitting a palace**
   The ***palatial*** estate had thirty-eight royally furnished rooms.

10. **perceptible** (pər·sĕp′tə·bəl), adj. **discernible, detectable, noticeable**
    Mother heard the scarcely ***perceptible*** sound of my sneaking a cookie.

Exercises

A *From vocabulary list 21, choose the word that best completes each sentence. (Note: You may have to change the tense or form of the word.)*

1. The ______________ child was punished by his mother.
2. My parents obtained a thirty-year ______________ when they bought their new house.
3. Mobs are often driven to violence by ______________ .
4. After receiving anesthesia, the patient became ______________ of his surroundings.
5. Simon of Cyrene helped Jesus carry the ______________ cross.
6. The stitches in the expertly tailored suit were barely ______________ .
7. The dehydrated men cried when they realized the oasis was only a ______________ .
8. Carbon monoxide is an odorless, colorless, and extremely ______________ gas.
9. The ______________ estate included a private amusement park.
10. Before walking into the Grand Hotel, Mrs. Brill attempted to straighten her ______________ hair.

B *In the space provided, write the vocabulary word from list 21 that is most nearly a* ***synonym*** *of the italicized expression.*

______________ 1. Chiggers are barely *observable* to the naked eye.

______________ 2. A Christian with a *slipshod, slovenly* appearance has a poor testimony for Christ.

______________ 3. The paint thinner's *unhealthy* fumes gave me a headache.

______________ 4. The principal told several *arrogant* students that he would not tolerate their disrespect.

______________ 5. The refraction of light rays shining on a highway can create a *vision* that looks just like water.

______________ 6. Do not think that God is *unmindful* of sin.

______________ 7. After Pilgrim asked for forgiveness, the *ponderous* burden rolled off his back.

______________ 8. The Taj Mahal is not a king's *grand, imposing* residence, but a tomb.

Review Exercises

Lists 15–21

A *In the following sentences, circle the vocabulary word in parentheses that best completes the meaning.*

1. In Bible times, a (*virtuous, voracious*) woman named Naomi desired to return to her home in Israel. Naomi could not (*solicit, stifle*) her daughter-in-law Ruth's desire to go along. Knowing that Naomi would be (*laden, oblivious*) with many responsibilities, Ruth desired to (*whet, allay*) them. Consequently, they (*embarked, complied*), trusting God to provide (*myriad, smug*) blessings.

2. My friends and I had a (*hysterical, kindred*) desire for a summer adventure. One afternoon, while exploring beyond the (*knoll, vestige*), we found a (*noxious, meandering*) path that led along a (*caustic, precarious*) ravine. The (*inestimable, incessant*) gurgling of water led us to the perfect swimming hole. That afternoon helped to satisfy our (*venturesome, corpulent*) spirits.

B *In each of the following groups, circle the word that is most nearly a* ***synonym*** *of the italicized word in the introductory phrase.*

1. to *distribute* the money in the defense budget
   (a) reconcile (b) allay (c) allocate (d) embark
2. outside the governor's *dominion*
   (a) perceptibility (b) jurisdiction (c) domicile (d) compliance
3. the vagabond's *unkempt* appearance
   (a) gaunt (b) murky (c) apt (d) disheveled
4. the *drawn tight* cables supporting the tower
   (a) gaunt (b) taut (c) compliant (d) allied
5. *dangerous,* storm-tossed seas
   (a) rapturous (b) insolent (c) placid (d) perilous
6. the disobedient servant, refusing to *consent*
   (a) comply (b) solicit (c) emit (d) connive
7. *unmindful* of her surroundings
   (a) perceptible (b) remorseful (c) oblivious (d) reconcilable

8. *bothered* by the information
   (a) accentuate (b) distraught
   (c) whet (d) solicit

9. taking medicine for the *lingering* cough
   (a) hysterical (b) pertinent
   (c) accentuated (d) chronic

10. a *neutral* negotiator
   (a) cordial (b) disinterested
   (c) caustic (d) jurisdictional

C

Match each vocabulary word with its definition.

	Definition		Word
________	1. set free from bondage, liberate		A. accentuate
________	2. emphasize, stress		B. brandish
________	3. supreme, unexcelled, unsurpassed		C. consumption
________	4. unhealthy emotion		D. disposition
________	5. fineness of taste, feeling, or thought		E. dispatch
________	6. covetous, greedy		F. dividend
________	7. uncertain, insecure		G. emancipate
________	8. sorrow, grief, regret		H. fetter
________	9. trace, track, sign		I. grasping
________	10. shake or wave menacingly		J. grotesque
________	11. magnificent, luxurious, befitting a palace		K. hysteria
________	12. self-satisfied, self-complacent		L. inestimable
________	13. incalculable, priceless		M. jargon
________	14. chain, shackle, confine		N. knoll
________	15. eating, devouring		O. minimize
________	16. share, portion, gain		P. mirage
________	17. small rounded hill		Q. palatial
________	18. send		R. precarious
________	19. bizarre, distorted, weird		S. refinement
________	20. a type of optical illusion		T. remorse
			U. smug
			V. superlative
			W. vestige

LIST

Spelling

Commonly misspelled words

1 **aisle**
2 **arise**
3 **Britain**
4 **cappuccino**
5 **career**
6 **competitor**
7 **concentrate**
8 **continuously**
9 **definition**
10 **during**
11 **heroes**
12 **inoculate**
13 **knowledge**
14 **later**
15 **noble**
16 **operations**
17 **prevalent**
18 **similar**
19 **stretch**
20 **tomorrow**

Note: A superscript number ([1], [2], etc.) after a word indicates the spelling rule on pages 4–5 which applies.

Vocabulary

1. **balmy** (bäm′ē), adj. **deliciously mild, soft, soothing**
   The ***balmy*** weather at Cades Cove was perfect for camping.

2. **chafe** (chāf), v. **anger, vex, irritate**
   One way to ***chafe*** the American people is to raise taxes.

3. **crevice** (krĕv′ĭs), n. **crack, cranny, chink**
   A little light shone through a ***crevice*** in the cave's roof.

4. **depreciate** (dĭ·prē′shē·āt), v. **undervalue, disparage, belittle**
   He seems to me to ***depreciate*** Shakespeare for the wrong reasons. —*T. S. Eliot*

5. **hoard** (hōrd), v. **accumulate, amass, treasure up**
   Thrifty consumers often ***hoard*** coupons in an effort to increase their purchasing power.

6. **infinity** (ĭn·fĭn′ĭ·tē), n. **boundlessness, endlessness, illimitableness**
   A knowledge of the ***infinity*** of God's power should have an effect on one's behavior.

7. **knack** (năk), n. **special ability, aptitude**
   Spenser, Milton, and Shakespeare had a ***knack*** for writing that few others can claim.

8. **morose** (mə·rōs′), adj. **glum, gloomy, sullen**
   His ***morose*** disposition left him with few friends.

9. **recess** (rē·sĕs′), n. **remote part or corner**
   A forgotten shoe lay in a ***recess*** of the closet.

10. **seethe** (sēth), v. **boil, bubble, foam**
    During a storm, waves break over the bow and ***seethe*** along the decks.

Exercises

A *From vocabulary list 22, choose the word that best completes each sentence. (Note: You may have to change the tense or form of the word.)*

1. Pyramus and Thisby often whispered to each other through a ______________________ in a wall.
2. The boys found gold way back in the ______________________ of an old cave.
3. Mrs. McCoy has a ______________________ for making ordinary meals taste delicious.
4. One whose eternity passes all time, and whose ______________________ passes all number, that is almighty God Himself. —*Tyndale*
5. At retirement, many people move to locations with ______________________ climates.
6. Burning the U. S. flag ______________________ the value of freedom.
7. The waves break upon the shore and ______________________ among the rocks.
8. Pack rats ______________________ such items as silverware, nails, and buckles.
9. Long lines at stores can easily ______________________ a person if he is in a hurry.
10. The ______________________ child sat pouting in his room.

B *Write the vocabulary word from list 22 that is most nearly a* **synonym** *of the italicized word.*

______________________ 1. The baked apples *simmered* in their own spicy juice.

______________________ 2. Refinishing an antique can *diminish* its value.

______________________ 3. Few things can *exasperate* a mother more than children fighting.

______________________ 4. Those are truly poor who *collect* things in this life and make no provision for eternity.

______________________ 5. Writing good poetry is a *talent* that not very many people have.

______________________ 6. A man should not give way to a *surly,* captious, and cavilling humor and be eager to find fault. —*Jortin*

______________________ 7. She enjoys relaxing in a shady *nook* of her flower garden.

______________________ 8. We all enjoyed the *pleasant* breezes of the Gulf of Mexico.

LIST 23

Spelling

Commonly misspelled words

1 **accurately**[4]
2 **article**
3 **carrying**[3]
4 **correlate**
5 **describe**
6 **endeavor**
7 **expense**
8 **hoping**[4]
9 **individual**
10 **likely**[4]
11 **maneuver**
12 **medicine**
13 **opponent**
14 **organization**[4]
15 **possess**
16 **religion**
17 **ridicule**
18 **sophomore**
19 **sufficient**[1]*
20 **useless**[4]

Note: A superscript number (1, 2, etc.) after a word indicates the spelling rule on pages 4–5 which applies. An asterisk (*) indicates an exception to the rule.

Vocabulary

1. **abyss** (ə·bĭs′), n. **bottomless pit, chasm**
   Satan will be bound and cast into the ***abyss*** for a thousand years.

2. **alternative** (ôl·tûr′nə·tĭv), n. **choice between two mutually exclusive things**
   Mason's idea was a good ***alternative*** to the original plan.

3. **commence** (kə·mĕns′), v. **begin**
   When will the meeting ***commence?***

4. **concerted** (kən·sûr′tĕd), adj. **cooperative, coordinated, combined**
   With a ***concerted*** effort, Nehemiah and his men rebuilt the walls of Jerusalem.

5. **conjecture** (kən·jĕk′tu͝r), v. **surmise, guess**
   I could not ***conjecture*** from the look on his face what he was thinking.

6. **decoy** (dē·koi′), v. **lure, entice**
   The hunter will ***decoy*** deer with salt licks.

7. **procure** (prō·kyo͝or′), v. **obtain by special effort**
   Did you ***procure*** the necessary forms?

8. **relentless** (rĭ·lĕnt′lĕs), adj. **unyielding, unsparing, merciless**
   Hitler's ***relentless*** attempt to exterminate the Jews was unsuccessful.

9. **tantalize** (tăn′tə·līz), v. **tease, torment, frustrate**
   He liked to ***tantalize*** children by offering them candy and then eating it himself.

10. **vigil** (vĭj′əl), n. **watch, lookout**
    Many businesses have security guards keeping ***vigil*** throughout the night.

Exercises

A *From vocabulary list 23, choose the word that best completes each sentence. (Note: You may have to change the tense or form of the word.)*

1. Meteorologists can only ________________ about next week's weather.
2. We can ________________ our puppy into his kennel by offering him a dog biscuit.
3. Michael ________________ the hard-to-get tickets for the playoff game.
4. Zachary kept ________________ all night by his mother's sickbed.
5. Hell is a(n) ________________ to be feared by all.
6. A championship team requires a ________________ effort by all.
7. Do not ________________ a person on a diet with sumptuous desserts.
8. With the bridge closed, our only ________________ was to turn around.
9. Congress will recess for the holidays and ________________ again in January.
10. The hurricane's ________________ winds caused much damage.

B *Write the vocabulary word from list 23 that is most nearly a* ***synonym*** *of the italicized word.*

________________ 1. Mr. Marks warned the boys not to *tease* his dog.

________________ 2. The officer's *surveillance* lead to an arrest.

________________ 3. The Roman guards subjected Christ to *pitiless* blows.

________________ 4. The men's *united* effort enabled them to paint the church by Sunday.

________________ 5. And beside all this, between us and you there is a great *gulf* fixed: so that they which would pass from hence to you cannot. . . . *—Luke 16:26*

________________ 6. We always *start* church with prayer.

________________ 7. Delilah *trapped* Samson with her charms.

________________ 8. For Patrick Henry, the only *option* to liberty was death.

________________ 9. Copernicus *hypothesized* and proved that the sun was the center of the solar system.

________________ 10. At an antique auction, Cecil managed to *attain* the masterpiece for his favorite client.

LIST **24**

Spelling

Commonly misspelled words

1 **adequately**[4]
2 **attempts**
3 **changing**[4]
4 **characteristic**
5 **create**
6 **despair**
7 **entertainment**
8 **fictitious**
9 **hundred**
10 **inevitable**
11 **liveliest**[3]
12 **paid**
13 **pamphlets**
14 **prejudice**
15 **response**
16 **sacrifice**
17 **sopranos**
18 **than**
19 **then**
20 **therefore**

Note: A superscript number ([1, 2,] etc.) after a word indicates the spelling rule on pages 4–5 which applies.

Vocabulary

1. **audacious** (ô·dā′shəs), adj. **bold, daring, adventurous**
   Walking a tightrope was an ***audacious*** stunt.

2. **bland** (blănd), adj. **smooth, suave, ingratiatingly pleasant**
   We disliked the salesman's ***bland*** manner.

3. **countenance** (koun′tə·nəns), n. **facial expression**
   Jenny's ***countenance*** revealed her delight in the gift.

4. **deteriorate** (dĭ·tîr′ē·ə·rāt), v. **worsen, decay**
   Poor eating habits caused my father's health to ***deteriorate.***

5. **emanate** (ĕm′ə·nāt), v. **issue, originate, derive**
   All earthly power ***emanates*** from God.

6. **engraft** (ĕn·grăft′), v. **implant, install, establish**
   Engraft Scripture into your life by memorizing it.

7. **genial** (jēn′yəl), adj. **cheerful, cordial, kindly**
   Mr. Grunch was uncharacteristically ***genial*** at the wedding.

8. **invariable** (ĭn·vâr′ĭ·ə·bəl), adj. **unchangeable, constant**
   The laws of God are ***invariable.***

9. **precipitous** (prĭ·sĭp′ĭ·təs), adj. **steep, abrupt**
   A Green Beret is able to rappel down the ***precipitous*** face of a cliff.

10. **vigilant** (vĭj′ə·lənt), adj. **watchful, wide-awake, alert**
    Be sober, be ***vigilant;*** because your adversary the devil, as a roaring lion, walketh about, seeking whom he may devour. *—I Pet. 5:8*

Exercises

A *From vocabulary list 24, choose the word that best completes each sentence. (Note: You may have to change the tense or form of the word.)*

1. The ______________________ man easily made new friends.
2. His deadpan ______________________ hid his underlying mirth.
3. Ethan Allen's ______________________ attack helped to capture Fort Ticonderoga.
4. Our standards of morality should be ______________________ .
5. The President's secret service men must always remain ______________________ .
6. Feudalism includes the idea that all rights ______________________ from a head landlord.
7. We crossed from one ______________________ cliff to the other by means of a rope bridge.
8. Relations between China and Russia ______________________ after World War II.
9. Stephen remained soothingly ______________________ during his persuasive speech.
10. Christians are branches ______________________ into the True Vine, Jesus Christ.

B *Write the vocabulary word from list 24 that is most nearly a* ***synonym*** *of the italicized word.*

______________________ 1. The rescue team descended the *perpendicular* wall of the gorge.

______________________ 2. The laws of nature are *immutable* and eternal. —*Hobbes*

______________________ 3. The soldier kept a *hawk-eyed* watch.

______________________ 4. Secularists can *ground* their false tenets only among those ignorant of God's truth.

______________________ 5. Mr. Johnson's *features* revealed much of his displeasure.

______________________ 6. The child's positive attitude *stems* from his parents'.

______________________ 7. The weather will quickly *decline* as a tornado approaches.

______________________ 8. The *intrepid* tamer stuck his head into the lion's mouth.

______________________ 9. The queen was disgusted with the *ingratiating* lord.

______________________ 10. The *affable* manager cheerfully greeted the customer.

Spelling

Commonly misspelled words

1 **affect**
2 **audience**[1]
3 **Christian**
4 **coming**[4]
5 **controversy**
6 **curious**
7 **effect**
8 **existent**
9 **ideally**
10 **interest**
11 **lonely**[4]
12 **mere**
13 **parliament**
14 **personal**
15 **personnel**
16 **prepare**
17 **prominent**
18 **revel**
19 **studying**[3]
20 **synonymous**

Note: A superscript number ([1, 2,] etc.) after a word indicates the spelling rule on pages 4–5 which applies.

Vocabulary

1. **courier** (ko͝or′ē·ər), n. **special messenger, carrier**
   Papyrus scrolls were delivered from place to place by ***couriers*** known for their speed.

2. **doting** (dōt′ĭng), adj. **excessively fond, indulgent, pampering**
   Doting mothers end by ruining their children.
   —Hallam Tennyson

3. **erratic** (ĕ·răt′ĭk), adj. **lacking direction, likely to change, undependable**
   A lack of goals often leads to ***erratic*** behavior.

4. **fledgling** (flĕj′lĭng), n. **rookie, trainee**
   The reporter, being just a ***fledgling,*** made several embarrassing mistakes.

5. **novel** (nŏv′əl), adj. **new, strange, original**
   The horseless carriage was a ***novel*** idea.

6. **permissible** (pər mĭs′ə bəl), adj. **allowable, not forbidden**
   Lying is not ***permissible*** for the Christian.

7. **pervade** (pər·vād′), v. **permeate, spread throughout**
   The strong smell of some adhesives can ***pervade*** the air.

8. **reconnoiter** (rē′kə·noi′tər), v. **survey, spy out**
   Scouts are sent ahead of the army to ***reconnoiter*** the terrain.

9. **surly** (sûr′lē), adj. **sullen, churlish, ill-tempered**
   Kaylie did not venture near the ***surly*** bulldog.

10. **whim** (hwĭm), n. **capricious notion, freakish idea**
    Todd had a sudden ***whim*** to eat liver.

Exercises

A *From vocabulary list 25, choose the word that best completes each sentence. (Note: You may have to change the tense or form of the word.)*

1. Twelve men entered Canaan to ____________________ the area for Joshua.
2. The skating instructor helped the ____________________ up off the ice.
3. I almost got into a car accident on the highway because a(n) ____________________ driver swerved into my lane.
4. Is staying out late on a weeknight ____________________ in your family?
5. "Sam, put it out of your mind," I snapped in a rather ____________________ rebuff. *—Michener*
6. The courageous ____________________ of the Pony Express carried the mail between Missouri and California.
7. The toddler dominated the attention of his ____________________ grandparents.
8. Her head must be filled with all kinds of ____________________ ideas.
9. Some get themselves into debt by acting upon a ____________________ .
10. The bubonic plague ____________________ Europe during the 1300s, killing a large percentage of the population.

B *Write the vocabulary word from list 25 that is most nearly a* ***synonym*** *of the italicized word.*

____________________ 1. *Lenient* parents make it difficult for children to do right.

____________________ 2. Griping, if not stopped early, can *penetrate* any group.

____________________ 3. An action based on *impulse* can result in disaster.

____________________ 4. Shareware is computer software that allows *unprohibited* downloading of a program.

____________________ 5. The general sent a team ahead to *scout out* the area for land mines.

____________________ 6. Though he had come in *sulky* unwillingness, he was impressed by the supper. *—Sinclair Lewis*

____________________ 7. A *beginner* rarely makes a hole in one.

____________________ 8. Paul, a *bearer* of the gospel, preached in Corinth.

____________________ 9. The telephone began as a *new-fangled* idea in the mind of Bell.

____________________ 10. I am always surprised by my crazy aunt's *unpredictable* behavior.

LIST 26

Spelling

Commonly misspelled words

1 **among**
2 **beneficial**
3 **Communist**
4 **controversial**[3]
5 **dependent**
6 **dilemma**
7 **escapade**
8 **everything**
9 **imagine**
10 **losing**
11 **magnificence**
12 **opinion**
13 **perceive**
14 **practical**
15 **safety**
16 **shining**[4]
17 **site**
18 **susceptible**
19 **theory**
20 **women**

Note: A superscript number ([1, 2,] etc.) after a word indicates the spelling rule on pages 4–5 which applies.

Vocabulary

1. **candid** (kăn′dĭd), adj. **unbiased, outspoken**
   The ***candid*** comment, while hurtful, was true.

2. **coincide** (kō′ĭn·sīd′), v. **agree, correspond exactly**
   Mom's and Dad's ideas about remodeling usually ***coincide.***

3. **foil** (foil), v. **defeat, frustrate, thwart**
   We hoped that nothing would ***foil*** our plans to go camping.

4. **garish** (gâr′ĭsh), adj. **gaudy, flashy, excessively bright**
   Miss Ima Flaunty thinks that ***garish*** clothing make her attractive.

5. **palatable** (păl′ət·ə·bəl), adj. **appetizing, tasty**
   The hostages' food in captivity was not ***palatable.***

6. **renegade** (rĕn′ĭ·gād), n. **traitor, apostate**
   Martin Luther stood for the truth of the Scriptures even though he knew the Roman church would mark him as a ***renegade.***

7. **retrieve** (rĭ·trēv′), v. **recover, regain**
   The Kuwaiti people hoped to ***retrieve*** some of their possessions stolen by the Iraqis.

8. **subjugate** (sŭb′jo͝o·gāt), v. **conquer and control**
   Communist North Vietnam was determined to ***subjugate*** South Vietnam.

9. **trivial** (trĭv′ĭ·əl), adj. **trifling, unimportant**
   Thinking school a ***trivial*** pastime, Hank sneaked away to the old swimming hole.

10. **unobtrusive** (ŭn′əb·tro͞o′sĭv), adj. **inconspicuous, unassuming, unassertive**
    Society usually tolerates undesirable groups as long as they remain ***unobtrusive.***

Exercises

A *From vocabulary list 26, choose the word that best completes each sentence. (Note: You may have to change the tense or form of the word.)*

1. Our team hopes to ____________________ our rival's plans to defeat us in the playoffs.
2. Marilyn asked Tammy for her ____________________ opinion on a dress.
3. Some people prefer the ____________________ neon lights of the city to the quiet beauty of the country.
4. Sometimes, an individual's plans for his life do not ____________________ with his best interests.
5. The Labrador splashed into the lake to ____________________ the duck that Steve had shot.
6. Grandmother is a(n) ____________________ person who quietly serves others.
7. Benedict Arnold turned ____________________ and tried to deliver West Point to the British.
8. Mother exhorted Sarah not to waste her time on ____________________ matters.
9. The root, when properly cooked, was converted into a ____________________ and nutritious food. *—Prescott*
10. Alexander the Great's army ____________________ the Fertile Crescent.

B *To complete this puzzle, choose the word from list 26 that is most likely to be associated with each clue below. Put each answer in the squares beginning with the number of the clue.*

1. to make someone a slave
2. meek and quiet
3. to squelch a plot to overthrow the king
4. to get back
5. happen together
6. delicious
7. purple, yellow, and orange dress with sequins
8. petty, inconsiderable ideas
9. a deserter
10. open-minded

List 26

Spelling

Commonly misspelled words

1 **all right**
2 **already**
3 **beauty**
4 **cite**
5 **comparative**
6 **define**
7 **destruction**
8 **experience**
9 **familiar**
10 **incidentally**
11 **led**
12 **manner**
13 **occurred**[2]
14 **pertain**
15 **politician**
16 **quiet**
17 **repetition**
18 **succession**
19 **surprise**
20 **writing**[4]

Note: A superscript number ([1,2] etc.) after a word indicates the spelling rule on pages 4–5 which applies.

Vocabulary

1. **foreshadow** (fōr·shăd′ō), v. **prefigure, foreshow**
   The ceremonies commanded in the law did ***foreshadow*** Christ. *—Luther*

2. **illustrate** (ĭl′əs·trāt), v. **demonstrate, give an example of**
   Our science teacher put a straw into a glass of water to ***illustrate*** the principle of refraction.

3. **invincible** (ĭn·vĭn′sə·bəl), adj. **unconquerable, unbeatable**
   The British tanks seemed ***invincible*** until the Germans manufactured antitank weapons.

4. **notorious** (nō·tō′rĭ·əs), adj. **infamous, ill-famed, dishonorable**
   Diocletian, a Roman emperor, is ***notorious*** for his persecution of Christians.

5. **plight** (plīt), n. **difficult condition or situation, predicament**
   It is difficult for Americans to imagine the ***plight*** of the starving masses in other countries.

6. **renowned** (rĭ nound′), adj. **famous, esteemed**
   Michelangelo is a ***renowned*** Renaissance painter.

7. **unprecedented** (ŭn·prĕs′ĭ·dĕn′tĕd), adj. **unheard of, unexampled**
   In 1832, the choosing of Presidential candidates by political conventions was ***unprecedented.***

8. **utilitarian** (yo͞o tĭl′ĭ târ′ē ən), adj. **useful, practical**
   These old dishes are ***utilitarian,*** not beautiful

9. **valid** (văl′ĭd), adj. **legal, lawful**
   Your driver's license must be renewed to remain ***valid.***

10. **vestibule** (vĕs′tə·byo͞ol), n. **entrance hall, lobby**
    A grandfather clock stood in the ***vestibule*** of the mansion.

Exercises

A *From vocabulary list 27, choose the word that best completes each sentence. (Note: You may have to change the tense or form of the word.)*

1. Can you recommend a plain, ____________________ motel to help us save money on our trip?
2. The artist used his drawing of a rose to ____________________ the beauty of God's designs.
3. When Bilbo was lost inside the mountain and met Gollum, he found himself in a terrible ____________________.
4. Many legal documents must be notarized to be ____________________.
5. Superman is ____________________ unless he is exposed to kryptonite.
6. Pharaoh's dream of seven fat cows ____________________ seven years of plenty.
7. We entered a brightly lit ____________________, which lead into the great hall.
8. The ____________________ criminal has finally been caught.
9. After Galileo invented his telescope, ____________________ views of the universe became possible.
10. The ____________________ district attorney won another victory against crime.

B *Write the vocabulary word from list 27 that is most nearly a* ***synonym*** *of the italicized word.*

____________________ 1. The *foyer* of the reception hall had a registration book for guests to sign.

____________________ 2. The *celebrated* author signed copies of his new book.

____________________ 3. The soccer team was *undefeatable* throughout the season.

____________________ 4. A birth certificate is not *legitimate* unless it has been notarized.

____________________ 5. I am looking for a *functional* cabinet for my office.

____________________ 6. Our church took an offering to help with the sad *dilemma* of the homeless.

____________________ 7. The teacher will *clarify* how a prism separates light waves.

____________________ 8. The *unparalleled* landing of the Apollo 11 astronauts on the moon captivated the world.

____________________ 9. Walter was *infamous* for bullying others on the playground.

LIST **28**

Spelling

Commonly misspelled words

1 **amount**
2 **argument**[4*]
3 **beginner**[2]
4 **competitive**
5 **conscious**
6 **different**[2]
7 **disastrous**
8 **explanation**
9 **fashions**
10 **independent**
11 **lose**
12 **maybe**
13 **occurring**[2]
14 **physical**
15 **possible**
16 **profession**
17 **separation**
18 **their**
19 **there**
20 **they're**

Note: A superscript number ([1, 2,] etc.) after a word indicates the spelling rule on pages 4–5 which applies. An asterisk (*) indicates an exception to the rule.

Vocabulary

1. **connoisseur** (kŏn′ə·sûr′), n. **expert in the arts, one with discriminating tastes**
   It takes much training to become a ***connoisseur*** of fine art.

2. **coup** (ko͞o), n. **brilliant strategic move, often a military overthrow of a government**
   Coup is short for *coup d'etat,* meaning a sudden overthrow of a government.

3. **imminent** (ĭm′ə·nənt), adj. **about to occur**
   The restlessness of the animals indicated that a storm was ***imminent.***

4. **incompatible** (ĭn′kəm·păt′ə·bəl), adj. **incapable of existing together, incongruous**
   Evolution and Creation are ***incompatible*** beliefs.

5. **prevalent** (prĕv′ə·lənt), adj. **widespread, common**
   The use of a word does not become correct just because it is ***prevalent.***

6. **sack** (săk), v. **plunder, strip, loot**
   The invading army intended to ***sack*** every village in its path.

7. **self-possessed** (sĕlf′pə·zĕst′), adj. **calm, composed, self-controlled**
   The ***self-possessed*** speaker was not intimidated by the hostile audience.

8. **solitude** (sŏl′ĭ·tūd), n. **aloneness, seclusion**
   Solitude brings no escape from spiritual danger. —*Vaughan*

9. **treacherous** (trĕch′ər·əs), adj. **untrustworthy, deceiving**
   The ***treacherous*** act caused the army's defeat.

10. **vacillate** (văs′ə·lāt), v. **hesitate, waver**
    Elijah told the people not to ***vacillate*** but to decide if they would serve God or Baal.

Exercises

A *From vocabulary list 28, choose the word that best completes each sentence. (Note: You may have to change the tense or form of the word.)*

1. The Black Death was ______________________ in western Europe from 1347 to 1351.
2. The lawyer always remained ______________________, even when defending unpopular cases.
3. Fred was unpopular because he always ______________________ when faced with a decision.
4. The Gap Theory attempts to merge Creation and Evolution, two completely ______________________ views.
5. The Romans ______________________ and totally destroyed Carthage.
6. We often are not aware of how ______________________ the wiles of the devil really are.
7. The Emergency Broadcasting System warns American citizens when danger is ______________________.
8. Landing the new account was a real ______________________ for the advertising executive.
9. A writer prefers ______________________ to avoid distractions.
10. Many chocolate ______________________ consider Swiss chocolates to be the best.

B *Write the vocabulary word from list 28 that is most nearly a* ***synonym*** *of each expression.*

1. isolation, separation, reclusion ______________________
2. current, widespread, common ______________________
3. impending, nigh, approaching ______________________
4. falter, fluctuate, be irresolute ______________________
5. confident, poised, level-headed ______________________
6. inharmonious, clashing, unsuitable ______________________
7. false, deceptive, unreliable ______________________
8. triumphant act ______________________
9. pillage, spoil, ravage ______________________
10. knowledgeable critic; authority in the field ______________________

Review Exercises
Lists 15–28

A

Circle the vocabulary word in parentheses that best completes the meaning.

1. There was certainly plenty of (*virtuous, valid*) evidence against the (*notorious, unprecedented*) criminal.
2. When he was burned at the stake, John Huss remained wholly (*self-possessed, disheveled*), having no cause for (*solicitation, remorse*) for having stood for the truth.
3. The (*vigilant, voracious*) squirrel watched for enemies as he (*hoarded, allocated*) acorns for the winter.
4. The (*pertinent, surly*) youth (*seethed, brandished*) with (*insolent, taut*) and slanderous language.
5. The seal wallowed on the (*mirage, shoal*) after escaping the (*precarious, cumbersome*) dangers of the (*smug, murky*) sea.

B

Circle the vocabulary word that is most nearly a **synonym** *of the italicized word in each phrase.*

1. a *winding* road
   (a) treacherous (b) relentless (c) grotesque (d) meandering
2. a *skill* for horseback riding
   (a) vestige (b) knack (c) disposition (d) courier
3. a *gloomy* attitude
   (a) balmy (b) concerted (c) morose (d) tacit
4. to *ruin* the villain's plans
   (a) brandish (b) fetter (c) foil (d) whet
5. refreshingly *new* idea
   (a) permissable (b) precarious (c) unobtrusive (d) novel
6. our *adventurous* mountain hike
   (a) precipitous (b) unprecedented (c) cumbersome (d) audacious
7. kept a *watch* over the flocks by night
   (a) domicile (b) jurisdiction (c) vigil (d) recess

8. a *sarcastic* remark
   (a) smug (b) chronic
   (c) garish (d) caustic

9. the *remote* hermit
   (a) genial (b) candid
   (c) aloof (d) audacious

10. praised the *priceless* painting
   (a) incompatible (b) inestimable
   (c) noxious (d) novel

C *Match each vocabulary word with its definition.*

_______ 1. appetizing, tasty
_______ 2. calm, quiet, peaceful
_______ 3. like, similar, agreeing
_______ 4. conquer and control
_______ 5. secretly plot to do wrong, scheme, conspire
_______ 6. cheerful, cordial, kindly
_______ 7. about to occur
_______ 8. unbiased by personal interest, impartial
_______ 9. hesitate, waver
_______ 10. capricious notion, freakish idea
_______ 11. dangerous, hazardous, risky
_______ 12. bottomless pit, chasm
_______ 13. unconquerable, unbeatable
_______ 14. plunder, strip, loot
_______ 15. enclose in a protective covering
_______ 16. undervalue, disparage, belittle
_______ 17. unyielding, unsparing, merciless
_______ 18. survey, spy out
_______ 19. facial expression
_______ 20. agree, correspond exactly

A. abyss
B. coincide
C. connive
D. countenance
E. depreciate
F. disinterested
G. emit
H. foreshadow
I. genial
J. imminent
K. insolent
L. invincible
M. kindred
N. palatable
O. perilous
P. placid
Q. reconnoiter
R. relentless
S. sack
T. subjugate
U. sheathe
V. vacillate
W. whim

Poetry

Footprints on the Sands

Henry Wadsworth Longfellow

Lives of great men all remind us
We can make our lives sublime,
And, departing, leave behind us
Footprints on the sands of time;

Footprints that perhaps another,
Sailing o'er life's solemn main,
A forlorn and shipwrecked brother,
Seeing, shall take heart again.

Let us, then, be up and doing,
With a heart for any fate;
Still achieving, still pursuing,
Learn to labor and to wait.

—from "Psalm of Life"

My Native Land

Sir Walter Scott

Breathes there the man, with soul so dead,
Who never to himself hath said,
  This is my own, my native land?
Whose heart hath ne'er within him burn'd,
As home his footsteps he hath turn'd
  From wandering on a foreign strand?
If such there breathe, go, mark him well;
For him no minstrel raptures swell;
High though his titles, proud his name,
Boundless his wealth as wish can claim,—
Despite those titles, power, and pelf,
The wretch, concentered all in self,
Living, shall forfeit fair renown,
And, doubly dying, shall go down
To the vile dust from whence he sprung,
Unwept, unhonor'd and unsung.

—*from* The Lay of the Last Minstrel

Sunrise and Sunset

Emily Dickinson

I'll tell you how the sun rose—
A ribbon at a time.
The steeples swam in amethyst,
The news like squirrels ran.

The hills untied their bonnets,
The bobolinks begun.
Then I said softly to myself,
"That must have been the sun!"

But how he set, I know not.
There seemed a purple stile
That little yellow boys and girls
Were climbing all the while

Till when they reached the other side,
A dominie in gray
Put gently up the evening bars,
And led the flock away.

Crossing the Bar

Alfred, Lord Tennyson

Sunset and evening star,
   And one clear call for me!
And may there be no moaning of the bar,
   When I put out to sea,

But such a tide as moving seems asleep,
   Too full for sound and foam,
When that which drew from out the boundless deep
   Turns again home.

Twilight and evening bell,
   And after that the dark!
And may there be no sadness of farewell,
   When I embark;

For tho' from out our bourne of Time and Place
   The flood may bear me far,
I hope to see my Pilot face to face
   When I have crost the bar.

Stopping by Woods on a Snowy Evening

Robert Frost

Whose woods these are I think I know.
His house is in the village, though;
He will not see me stopping here
To watch his woods fill up with snow.

My little horse must think it queer
To stop without a farmhouse near
Between the woods and frozen lake
The darkest evening of the year.

He gives his harness bells a shake
To ask if there is some mistake.
The only other sound's the sweep
Of easy wind and downy flake.

The woods are lovely, dark, and deep,
But I have promises to keep,
And miles to go before I sleep,
And miles to go before I sleep.

O Captain! My Captain!

Walt Whitman

O Captain! my Captain! our fearful trip is done,
The ship has weather'd every rack, the prize we sought is won
The port is near, the bells I hear, the people all exulting,
While follow eyes the steady keel, the vessel grim and daring;

But O heart! heart! heart!
O the bleeding drops of red,
Where on the deck my Captain lies,
Fallen cold and dead.

O Captain! my Captain! rise up and hear the bells;
Rise up—for you the flag is flung—for you the bugle trills,
For you bouquets and ribbon'd wreaths—for you the shores
a-crowding,
For you they call, the swaying mass, their eager faces turning.

Here Captain! dear father!
This arm beneath your head!
It is some dream that on the deck,
You've fallen cold and dead.

My Captain does not answer, his lips are pale and still,
My father does not feel my arm, he has no pulse nor will,
The ship is anchor'd safe and sound, its voyage closed and done,
From fearful trip the victor ship comes in with object won:

Exult O shores, and ring O bells!
But I with mournful tread,
Walk the deck my Captain lies,
Fallen cold and dead.

Be True

Horatius Bonar

Thou must be true thyself,
  If thou the truth wouldst teach;
Thy soul must overflow, if thou
  Another's soul would'st reach!
It needs the overflow of heart
  To give the lips full speech.

Think truly, and thy thoughts
  Shall the world's famine feed;
Speak truly, and each word of thine
  Shall be a fruitful seed;
Live truly, and thy life shall be
  A great and noble creed.

The Flag Goes By

Henry Holcomb Bennett

Hats off!
Along the street there comes
A blare of bugles, a ruffle of drums,
A flash of color beneath the sky:
Hats off!
The flag is passing by.

Blue and crimson and white it shines,
Over the steel-tipped, ordered lines.
Hats off!
The colors before us fly;
But more than the flag is passing by.

Sea-fights and land-fights, grim and great,
Fought to make and save the State:
Weary marches and sinking ships;
Cheers of victory on dying lips;

Days of plenty and years of peace;
March of a strong land's swift increase;
Equal justice, right, and law,
Stately honor and reverend awe;

Sign of a nation, great and strong
To ward her people from foreign wrong:
Pride and glory and honor,—all
Live in the colors to stand or fall.

Hats off!
Along the street there comes
A blare of bugles, a ruffle of drums;
And loyal hearts are beating high:
Hats off!
The flag is passing by!

Song from Pippa Passes

Robert Browning

The year's at the spring
And day's at the morn;
Morning's at seven;
The hillside's dew-pearled;
The lark's on the wing;
The snail's on the thorn;
God's in His heaven—
All's right with the world!